£11.99

CareFully

A GUIDE FOR
HOME CARE ASSISTANTS

Lesley Bell

THIS BOOK IS FOR
REFERENCE ONLY
AND IS NOT TO BE REMOVED

D0294474

BISHOP AUCKLAND COLLEGE
LEARNING RESOURCE LIBRARY
ACCESSION NO. 190184
CLASS NO. 362.6

ACE
BOOKS

© ACE Books 1993
Published by Age Concern England
1268 London Road
London SW16 4ER

Editor Gillian Clarke
Production Marion Peat
Design Eugenie Dodd
Printed and bound in Great Britain by Bell & Bain Ltd, Glasgow.

A catalogue record for this book is available from the British Library.

ISBN 0–86242–129–2

All rights reserved, no part of this work may be reproduced
in any form, by mimeograph or any other means, without
permission in writing from the publisher.

Contents

Appendices

About the Author

Since 1988 Lesley Bell has headed the work of the Joint Initiative for Community Care Ltd, an organisation that has a remit to work across boundaries in relation to community care. In 1991 JICC became a registered charity, owned jointly by the Association of Directors of Social Services and Local Government Management Board. She is also a non-executive director of Bedford and Shires Community and Health Trust.

Prior to setting up JICC, Lesley was a senior training adviser for 11 years in the Local Government Training Board, where she was responsible for the development of training recommendations and training material for home care assistants, home care managers and care assistants in homes for older people. She is Chair of the Joint Advisory Group of Domiciliary Care Associations, and a Trustee of BADCO (British Association of Domiciliary Care Associations).

Lesley has undertaken a number of activities in relation to community care. She was Project Manager for the development of the OPAL Package – Open and Assisted Learning for Community Care Managers – on behalf of NALGO Education. On behalf of the Department of Health, she has been involved in determining the training needs of people who undertake care management activities. She was also manager of the Craven Community Care Project, funded by the Joseph Rowntree Foundation.

Lesley has undertaken considerable work on the development of managers throughout the Personal Social Services. She was author of the Department of Health's guidance on management development, published in April 1990, in relation to the Training Support Programme. She speaks regularly at seminars, conferences and workshops and is a frequent contributor to professional journals.

Acknowledgements

Thanks are due to many people who contributed to the compilation of this book. However, particular thanks are due to the following:

John Bellingall, who assisted in writing the script and without whom it would not have been possible to produce this book in the time available.

Kent County Council Social Services Department for permission to use material from *Good Care – A guide to the good care of elderly people living at home.*

Local Government Management Board for permission to extract information from training and information material relating to home care.

Surrey County Council Social Services Department for permission to use material from 'Guidelines for Good Practice' for Home Care Assistants.

Trevor Jones from Leicestershire County Council Social Services Department for inspiration for the title *Carefully.*

The Officers and others from those associations and authorities who read through the script and commented on the draft material, including:

The British Association of Domiciliary Care Officers, The Carers Unit, Kings Fund Centre, Kent County Council Social Services Department, London Borough of Hammersmith and Fulham Social Services Department, The National Council of Domiciliary Care Services, The Royal National Institute for the Blind, Social Care Association, Surrey County Council Social Services Department, The United Kingdom Home Care Association, Warwickshire County Council Social Services Department.

Lesley Bell
July 1993

Introduction

The provision of care to people in their own homes is an area of work that is of vital importance to people receiving care and to their family, friends and neighbours. It enables them to remain in their own homes for as long as possible, by providing support when they are unable to care entirely for themselves, whether as a result of frailty, illness or disability, and may therefore be vulnerable to further incapacity.

There is no doubt that providing care to people in their own homes can be very rewarding work – and at the same time very demanding. The vast majority of those involved in the provision of home care are extremely committed and dedicated people who frequently undertake tasks that are over and above those that they are formally required to do.

Yet the work undertaken by Home Care Assistants (or Home Carers) – like so many other similar areas of work, such as nursing – has been consistently overlooked, undervalued and taken for granted by those in positions of power and authority in particular and by society in general. This is not a situation that will continue.

Home care is changing

The needs that people have for care are becoming more complex and demanding. Recent legislation relating to community care places an increasing emphasis on the provision of care to people in their own homes; you will read more about this in Chapter 1 – 'Home Care in Context'. There will be an increase in the number and type of organisations providing home care and an increase in the number of people involved.

Why home care is different

As someone who provides care for people in their own homes, you will have your own reasons for wishing to be involved in this area of work. Many Home Care Assistants have had experience of providing personal care for a relative and bringing up a family. Others have been trained as nurses or nursing auxiliaries. The one feature that all involved in the provision of home care have in common is the desire to work with people and to help them as far as possible and practical.

A second distinctive feature of the provision of home care is that you will generally be working on your own, in someone else's home, with no colleagues to refer to quickly in particular situations, or when things go wrong or an accident occurs. In these situations both the person receiving the care and you, the person providing it, are vulnerable. The result of the action or decision you take at the time, in the circumstances, can be very important.

Some Home Care Assistants work in pairs or in teams but this is still relatively unusual. It is much more usual for Home Care Assistants to work on their own, although as part of a larger network of people such as those delivering 'meals on wheels', community nurses and occupational therapists, all of whom may also be providing care and nursing services to the same person in their own home.

How this book can assist

CareFully has been written as a practical guide, to help you in your work, whether you are a new Home Care Assistant or already have some experience. It provides information, hints and ideas. It is designed to be easy to read and refer to. There are checklists for quick reference and case studies that provide real examples of situations encountered by Home Care Assistants.

This book is designed to help you in your work now, and also to help you prepare for the future by taking account of the changes taking place in community care and in home care.

Some employing organisations may find some of the suggestions and recommendations in this book difficult to put into practice. However, every effort has been made to reflect what is considered to be good practice in the provision of home care, and all employing organisations should recognise the need to take appropriate action and work towards ensuring the provision of a high quality service.

In providing home care you may be employed by one of any number of different organisations. You may work for one of the many voluntary organisations that are increasingly providing care for people in their own homes or you may work for a local authority social services department (SSD). If you work for a private agency, you may be employed directly by that agency or you may be self-employed and paid directly by the person being cared for, with the agency in the middle, acting as the contractor, introducing you to people who have care needs.

Whatever the exact nature of your employment and employing organisation, this book has been written with you in mind. Similarly your job title. *CareFully* uses the title 'Home Care Assistant' but there are other job titles that are actually used in practice, including Home Carer, Domiciliary Care Assistant and the original title Home Help. *CareFully* encompasses the work of all who undertake similar activities, irrespective of the actual job title applied or the nature of the employing organisation.

In the Appendices to this book you will find a number of checklists. Appendix 2 is particularly important as it relates to information on formal policies and practices which you should expect to be provided by your employing organisation. You need this information to enable you to do your job properly. If they don't provide this information, ask them for it!

There is also a checklist identifying the components of a quality service, extracted from each of the chapters of this book. Another checklist brings together all the issues in each chapter of this book that need to be referred to your line manager or some other appropriate person for action or information.

Yet another checklist is on training. It identifies the national developments currently taking place in training, relates the content of each chapter of this book to the relevant competency units in the new National Vocational Qualification (NVQ) in Health and Social Care, and identifies the broad areas of in-service training need.

The information contained in this book will also be of use to others involved in providing home care, in particular people providing care on a voluntary and unpaid basis, either as personal carers, looking after relatives and sometimes friends, often for 24 hours a day, or as volunteers, generally attached to a community organisation such as a local church or a voluntary organisation. *CareFully* should also be of interest and use to nursing auxiliaries and others working for health authorities and trusts, in the community.

This book can also be used as useful reference material for line managers, training officers and employing organisations, to assist in the supervision of staff. It provides basic training as well as reference material.

Conclusion

No one knows how many people work as Home Care Assistants. There is no accurate information available. A reasonably informed estimate puts the total figure at somewhere around 150,000 people. The one thing that is certain is that you are not alone.

There are many other people undertaking the same or similar work as you. *CareFully* should assist with that work.

1 Home Care in Context

This first chapter discusses the work of a Home Care Assistant with regard to the range of people who need care in their own homes, including people from ethnic minority communities; the needs, rights and expectations of people receiving care; and the implications for the provision of home care of the community care legislation and Government Guidance, including complaints procedures.

WHO NEEDS CARE?

It is worth remembering that the vast majority of people are able to care for themselves, in their own homes, possibly with the support of relatives and/or friends. They never have a need for a Home Care Assistant, other than perhaps someone paid to undertake the household and domestic tasks on a regular basis.

Nevertheless, many people need extra help and support at some stage in their lives. This may be the result of temporary illness, disability or other difficulty, which means that they require assistance for a short period of time, until they are fully recovered and are able to completely care for themselves again.

Other people may have a continuing, long-term need for care and support. This could be for one or more of the following reasons:

Physical disability, such as frailty, being unable to walk and/or using a wheelchair.

Physical illness which becomes progressively worse, such as Alzheimer's disease (dementia), multiple sclerosis, muscular dystrophy and HIV-related illnesses (see Appendix 6 for explanations of these terms).

Sensory impairment, such as hearing or sight loss.

Learning disabilities (previously commonly referred to as mental handicap).

People with mental health problems.

Over 90 per cent of care and support is provided by personal carers – family and friends of the person requiring assistance. Less than 10 per cent is provided by paid Home Care Assistants. However, they are a vital and essential source of assistance to people with care needs who live on their own. Increasingly, Home Care Assistants also provide relief and assistance to family carers in order to support them and enable them to continue to provide care on a long-term basis.

We have an ageing population in the United Kingdom. In 1990 there were nearly 4 million people in the population aged 75 and over. That number will increase throughout this decade and into the twenty-first century. This is the result of people living longer. In addition, a significant fall in the birth rate in the 1970s and early 1980s means that older people, of pensionable age, represent a larger percentage of the population (18.27 per cent in 1990) than they did 15 and 20 years earlier. (Age Concern England can provide a handy factcard on these statistics.)

It is very likely that, as a Home Care Assistant, most of the people you will be caring for will be aged 75 and over. However, some people will be 'younger' older people, between the ages of 65 and 74. Still others will be adults aged between 18 and 64 who, because of some form of disability, are only able to live in their own homes and care for themselves with the help and support that a Home Care Assistant can provide.

Home Care Assistants also provide care, help and support to families with children. This is generally on a short-term basis as the result of:

- illness;
- family circumstances;
- birth of another child or multiple birth;
- inability to cope – for whatever reason.

As a Home Care Assistant you will probably, in time, provide care to all these people on an individual basis. It is important not to generalise about people and their care needs, to recognise that each person will have their own individual needs, preferences and wishes, and to respond appropriately to each, according to the needs of the particular situation.

PRINCIPLES FOR THE PROVISION OF HOME CARE

There are a series of principles or values that should underpin the provision of care to people in their own home. These principles should apply to each and every one of us, regardless of whether we have a particular need for personal care.

The principles have been generally accepted by the wide range of organisations involved in providing care, and are adapted from *Home Life: A code of practice for residential care* (see p 151). These principles are summarised as follows:

Fulfilment – to enable each individual to achieve fully what they are capable of physically, intellectually, emotionally and socially.

Dignity the preservation of individual self-respect, particularly of people who are dependent upon the care and support of others.

Autonomy and **individuality** – the recognition and acceptance of the need for people to make their own decisions and choices.

Independence – the need to maintain, support and encourage personal independence, including the degree of risk this may entail.

Esteem – the recognition of the qualities, experiences, abilities and talents of each individual person.

Quality of experience – the need to enable people to experience and be involved in as wide a range of normal everyday activities as possible. This is particularly important for people who are unable to get out of their home.

Emotional needs – recognition of the needs every person has for emotional expression and fulfilment, particularly in their personal relationships with others.

In order to provide a high-quality service to the people you care for, you should think about the principles that are identified. Do you agree with them? How can you incorporate them into your day-to-day work? What do you think they really mean in practice for you and the people you are caring for?

The rights of people receiving care

The principles given above may be thought of as a series of **rights**. As a Home Care Assistant you have a responsibility to the people you are caring for, to recognise and protect their rights. Together, the **principles** identified above and the **rights** spelt out below provide the **values**, which should be the basis of all the care you provide to people living in their own homes.

The **rights** of each individual person include:

- The right to **privacy** and **confidentiality**.
- The right to be **listened to** and to have wishes and opinions considered.
- The right to **respect** and not to be demeaned (ie literally, to lower in dignity).
- The right to have **freedom of movement** and of not being restricted by, for example, being kept in a locked room or home.
- The right to be allowed to **take risks**.
- The right **not** to be **discriminated against** for any reason; for example, race, age, religion, colour, disability, sexual orientation, physical and financial circumstances.
- The right to **personal choice**, according to individual preferences whenever and wherever possible.
- The right to be **addressed** in the way each individual person chooses and prefers, and to have one's personal first name used only on freely given consent.
- The right to have access to preferred **religious leaders**.
- The right to **eat** and **drink** according to own preferences, only being advised by appropriate people on the advantages and dangers of certain foods and of the dangers of excessive smoking and alcohol consumption.
- The right to **make one's own decisions** – which may conflict with others, for example professionals and/or with the family view.

- The right to have **access to friends** and **relatives** and to be given assistance to see them, if necessary.
- The right to **have a pet** if able to care for and look after it.
- The right **not** to be **coerced** to participate in activities against one's wishes and desires (eg singing, playing games).
- The right to say **no**!

This list of rights is not comprehensive. Can you think of any others that you would add?

The organisation for which you work may have its own list of principles, values for service delivery or rights. Obtain a copy and compare it to the lists above. Identify the similarities and the differences.

If your organisation does not have such a list, do you think it should have one? These lists could provide a starting point. You will find another list of rights in Appendix 1. This has been written as a **charter of rights** for people receiving home care from Surrey County Council Social Services Department. You will see that the Surrey list of rights is specifically related to the provision of home care services, while the list of rights above is more general.

Protecting people's rights

Many of these rights are very difficult to protect in practice. The need to safeguard confidentiality is essential, yet you may be given information by the person you are caring for that makes you concerned for their continued health or safety, and makes it necessary to pass on the information to their GP or your line manager. In these circumstances, always seek permission to tell others.

Never pass information on to others, including relatives and friends of the person receiving care, without that person's permission.

Someone who has poor sight may prefer private correspondence to be read to them by a Home Care Assistant, rather than by a member of the family, knowing that confidentiality will be observed and that no comment will be made on the content.

On occasions a person who is suffering from Alzheimer's disease, and is therefore confused, may wander around, outside the home, at night, often in an undressed state. The obvious and least drastic remedy is to lock them in the home, but that takes away their personal right to freedom of movement.

Another example is the right to make one's own decisions. This can be a difficult area, which can lead to disagreement, particularly when the decision of the individual person conflicts with the wishes of the relatives. However, the only limitation on this right should be where the medically diagnosed mental condition of the person indicates that she or he is not capable of self-determination.

It is a good test for you as a Home Care Assistant to place yourself in the position of the person you are caring for, read through the list of rights again and ask yourself how important those rights are to you. How would you feel if they were taken away or ignored? Ask yourself, 'How would I react?'

Most older people say that they feel the same inside as they did when they were younger. If they feel the same, why should they be treated any differently? How do you feel? Do you feel the same as you did 20 years ago? Would you expect to be treated any differently?

You as a Home Care Assistant should **always** treat all the people you are caring for in exactly the same way as you would wish to be treated yourself.

CARING FOR PEOPLE FROM ETHNIC MINORITY COMMUNITIES

The **rights** identified above include the right not to be discriminated against, for whatever reason, and the right to individual choice and preference. The United Kingdom is a multi-racial, multi-cultural society and this should be reflected in the way in which care is provided to people from ethnic minority communities, living in their own homes.

Never assume that ethnic minority communities care for people from their own community. Older people from ethnic communities can be just as isolated and in need of care as others, whatever their religious and cultural background.

People who belong to ethnic minority communities have a right to expect a Home Care Assistant to fully understand their needs and to respect their cultural and religious requirements. Ideally, they should also have the right to expect to have a carer, if they wish, from their own ethnic or religious community or background. This is not always possible, though.

Most employing organisations will try to match the needs of all people requiring home care with the skills, characteristics, cultural and religious background of the Home Care Assistants they have available (see also Chapter 3). However, a perfect match is often difficult to achieve, particularly when meeting the care needs of people from ethnic minority communities.

You should never be expected to provide care to people from ethnic communities without undertaking the appropriate and necessary training. Otherwise, it shows disrespect to the person you will be caring for and conflicts with many of the personal rights that were identified.

Think about how different religious and cultural backgrounds could affect the way in which you provide care to people from ethnic minority communities. This is followed up further in Chapter 3.

Just as people with care needs have a right not to be discriminated against, so do Home Care Assistants. If you consider that you are the subject of discrimination by the person you are caring for, you should always report the problem to your employing organisation and line manager.

COMMUNITY CARE AND THE HOME CARE SERVICE

The National Health Service and Community Care Act 1990 introduced new requirements for community care, phased in from April 1993. These new requirements place home care at the heart of the provision of effective community care.

The detail of putting the law into practice will not directly affect Home Care Assistants themselves, although there will be considerable implications for the managers of your employing organisation and, in the medium to longer term, for the development of the Home Care Service as a whole and for the nature of the work undertaken by Home Care Assistants.

The Government, in the White Paper, 'Caring for People – community care in the next decade and beyond', has identified the following six key objectives for community care:

- To promote the development of domiciliary, day and respite services to enable people to live in their own homes wherever feasible and sensible.
- To ensure that service providers make practical support for carers a high priority.
- To make assessment of need and good care management the basis of high-quality care.
- To promote the development of a flourishing independent sector alongside good-quality public services.
- To clarify the responsibilities of agencies and to make it easier to hold them to account for their performance.
- To secure better value for taxpayers' money by introducing a new funding structure for social care.

The provision of home care is essential to the achievement of these six key objectives.

Firstly, home care is the foundation of effective community care: it is the main service responsible for providing care and supporting people in their own homes. Because more people, through their own choice, will probably be cared for in their own homes who would have previously entered a residential home, it is likely that, in time, the care needs of people living in their own homes will become more complex, more demanding and challenging.

In complex cases it is very likely that other professional staff such as community and district nurses will also be providing care services. You are then likely to find yourself working as a part of a multi-disciplinary team, all providing essential care to the person in their own home.

Secondly, the Government places great emphasis on the need to provide support to personal carers – family and friends who, as we identified earlier in this chapter, provide over 90 per cent of the care for people in their own homes, often on a 24-hour basis 365 days a year. In these circumstances the regular provision of a Home Care Assistant to share the tasks and to provide relief can often contribute significantly to supporting the family carer; it will help them to continue to provide the care and so prevent a breakdown in the care arrangements that would otherwise lead to a person going into residential care.

In these situations it will be essential that you as the Home Care Assistant are able to work with and relate to both the person with care needs and their personal family carer. (See also Chapter 2.)

Thirdly, the Government wishes to ensure that people with care needs and their relatives are involved in decisions relating to the care they receive and that, wherever possible and practicable, they are given choice in the nature of and way in which the care services are provided. This is part of what is known as developing a 'needs-led' approach rather than 'service-led'. This means that the person receiving care is the focus and that the care services you provide should be those specifically required by that person and in line with the local authority's priorities (needs-led), not those which either the organisation you work for or the social services department that has assessed the needs decides are available (service-led).

Fourthly, the Government is concerned that local authority social services departments should not continue to have the near-monopoly of providing home care services that they have had until recently. They are therefore taking action to encourage the development of new approaches to the provision of home care, based in voluntary organisations, private and not-for-profit agencies. This is known as the 'mixed economy of care provision'. You may work for one of these organisations or for the social services department; whichever you work for, you are increasingly likely to have contact with Home Care Assistants from a wide range of different agencies.

Contracting the provision of services

One of the principal outcomes from developing a range of organisations providing home care services is that the service will be increasingly 'purchased' from organisations and units providing care services (such as the one you work for). The purchase will be made by the local authority social services departments, on the basis of some form of contract, on behalf of people they have assessed as having a need for home care.

This situation is likely to apply to you, even if you work in a local authority social services department. Most departments now differentiate between their 'purchasing' and 'commissioning' function – which means the part of the organisation that is responsible for placing contracts and buying services to meet the care needs of people – and the part of the organisation in which you work, which actually provides the service that is required. This is often referred to as the 'purchaser/provider split'.

This 'purchasing' or 'commissioning' process will lead to the development of two forms of 'contract', both of which you need to be aware of:

1   The 'contract' between the social services department and the person whose needs have been assessed for the provision of home care. This is known as the **care plan**. You need to know the detail of the plan and/or the assessed needs to be sure that you are meeting all the care needs that have been identified, that you are undertaking all the required tasks and that you are not going beyond your duties. You also need to know what other organisations (if any) are also providing care services to the same person, so that you can work together if necessary.

2   The 'contract' for service provision between the social services department and your employing organisation or unit. Your line manager and the managers of the organisation will want to be sure that you provide care to the standard required and within the costs specified in the contract and that the work you undertake does not break or go beyond conditions of the 'contract' in any way.

A third form of contract also exists, generally on an informal basis, between you as the Home Care Assistant and the person you are caring for. This 'contract' relates to the tasks you and the person receiving care agree should be undertaken, and the way in which they are done. This is explored further in Chapter 2.

Components of the care plan

Some or all of the following information should be included in the care plan that is compiled for each person. The exact content of the plan will vary depending upon the assessed care needs of individuals and the complexity of the plan.

■   Assessed care needs including the abilities and capabilities of each person.

- Priorities in meeting care needs.
- How it has been agreed that the care needs will be met – and any disagreement.
- Others involved, including family carers and health staff, and when.
- Principal point of contact (family and service-providing organisation).
- Any particular medical conditions.
- Any special dietary requirements.
- Individual personal preferences that affect the provision of care.
- Any health and safety hazards that have been identified.
- Ways of maintaining independence and acknowledged risks that have been identified.

The Home Care Assistant as the 'keyworker'

As a Home Care Assistant you will be the one person (other than relatives or friends) who will be in the most frequent and regular contact with the person requiring care. This role is sometimes called that of **keyworker**. You are therefore in the best position to judge if those care needs have changed, if the situation and circumstances have altered and if further help and support are required.

Any such changes should always be reported to your line manager and/or employing organisation to enable them to take appropriate action. However tempting it is to do 'that bit extra' for the person you are caring for, you should never try to meet the further needs yourself without the agreement of your employer, because that could be breaking the terms of the contract between the social services department 'purchasing' care from your employing organisation. You may also find that in certain circumstances (eg climbing ladders) it cancels any occupational insurance under which you are covered by your employer.

One of the many significant outcomes of the emphasis on caring for people in the community is that many people, in particular those with learning disabilities, who previously lived in large institutions and hospitals are now living in their own homes in the community. You may find that you and other Home Care Assistants will be working more and more with people with learning disabilities, providing them with care where necessary and helping them to make the most of their own abilities and be as independent as possible, either individually or living with others in very small groups in their own homes.

Finally, in relation to community care, you may come across the terms 'care assessment' and 'care management'. These are specific activities undertaken in order to compile the **care plan** for the person requiring care, and will not generally directly involve you. What does concern you, however, is that, at the end of the day, the Government policy of community care, providing care for vulnerable people in their own homes, can succeed only if you, the Home Care Assistant, have the skills, abilities and commitment to undertake your part of the care plan for each person that you are caring for and ensure that they receive a high-quality service.

COMPLAINTS

The National Health Service and Community Care Act 1990 required all social services departments to put in place and publicise a formal complaints procedure by April 1991, to try to ensure that complaints from people needing care and their families are investigated and dealt with in a structured and positive way. The intention is that a proper complaints procedure can provide safeguards and protection both for people receiving care services and, in the case of unjustified or malicious complaints, for staff.

Although only social services departments have to have formal complaints procedures by law, it will become increasingly necessary for voluntary organisations and private agencies to have their own complaints procedures.

If you are employed by a social services department, you need to be aware of the department's complaints procedure; indeed, it should form part of your initial induction training.

If you are employed by a voluntary or private sector agency, ask what their policy and procedure are with regard to complaints. If they don't have a specific policy on it now, it's unlikely to be very long before they find that they need one.

If you follow the guidance in this book, it is unlikely, but not impossible, that any of the people you are caring for will make a complaint against you and the service you are providing. Nevertheless, you need to be well informed about the complaints procedure because the people you are caring for will almost certainly have been told about it – and if they haven't been told, they should have!

Remember that a person who has difficulty seeing properly and has sight problems may not be fully aware of the complaints procedure. They should be encouraged to seek information from the social services department or from your employer and ask for it to be sent to them in a suitable form such as an audio tape or braille.

In reality, the vast majority of complaints about the provision of care to people in their own homes are likely to focus on differences of opinion on the assessment of need between the professionals on one hand and the person needing care and/or their family on the other. Although every effort will be made to resolve such differences of opinion, at the end of the day the complaints procedure is the last course of action. As a Home Care Assistant you must be aware of this, if any of the people you are caring for find themselves in this situation.

If you work for an agency that is providing care services under some form of contractual agreement on behalf of a social services department, you also need to be aware that the SSD's complaints procedure is also there to be used by any of your service users and their families who, for whatever reason, are not satisfied with the care service they are receiving.

Components of a complaints procedure

Typical components of a complaints policy are that it should:

- be well defined and publicised;
- define exactly what a complaint is;
- recognise that agencies, and their staff, are not perfect;
- recognise that users have a right to challenge decisions made by the agency and information held about them;
- be part of, and not a substitute for, good practice.

The procedure itself

The complaints procedure should:

- recognise that service users may be vulnerable and/or powerless and, as a result, afraid to use a complaints procedure;
- allow for and encourage service users to make use of advocates (ie independent people who will help them make out their case or speak on their behalf and represent their interests);
- be part of the organisation and not 'added on' to it;
- be simple to understand and to operate;
- involve staff, and unions (if appropriate), and allow them to give their views;
- indicate where and when criminal proceedings are appropriate;
- recognise that some users will not complain, despite having a good cause or reason (lack of complaints may not be an indication that all is well but, rather, that people find it difficult to complain).

A complaint should become formal only after all informal channels of resolution have been exhausted.

Don't resist complaints. They can help you provide a better service. However, as the Home Care Assistant you will often be the first person, on the spot, able to put things right before they become a formal complaint. Putting things right first time can often save a lot of work, worry and anxiety later.

Think how you will feel if someone you are caring for complains about what you are doing or how you are doing it. What action will you take?

It is important to recognise that a very few people always complain about everything. There will be nothing you can do to please or satisfy them. In these circumstances the formal complaints procedure is there to protect you as well.

Always inform your line manager if you think a complaint may be made against you, for whatever reason. If you are a member of a trade union, they may also be able to help you. If you have provided the care services to the standard specified, you should have nothing to fear.

KEY POINTS

- Over 90 per cent of all care at home is provided by personal family carers.

- Most people Home Care Assistants care for are aged 75+; some will be younger adults with disabilities. You may also provide care and support to families with children.

- It is always important to see each person as an individual in their own right, with their own needs, preferences, etc.

- There are a series of **principles** and **rights** which should form the basis of all the care provided to people in their own homes.

- People who belong to ethnic minority communities have a right to expect Home Care Assistants to respect their cultural and religious norms and requirements.

- The provision of effective home care lies at the heart of community care and the achievement of the six key objectives.

- Home Care Assistants should be aware of the contents of the **care plan**, drawn up for each person as a result of assessment of their care needs.

- Wherever possible, people needing care and their families should be involved in decisions about the home care they receive and, when possible, given choices in the sort of care and the way in which it is provided.

- Home Care Assistants should also be aware in general terms of any conditions within the contract to provide services, between their employing organisation/unit and the SSD purchasing the service, that will affect the way in which they do their work.

- Make sure you obtain a copy of your local SSD's complaints procedure, and that for your own organisation if it is different. Some, if not all, of the people you are caring for will be aware of it and may use it.

2 Enter You, the Home Care Assistant

This chapter explores the nature of the relationship between you, the Home Care Assistant, the person you are caring for and their immediate family and friends. It considers the particular needs of carers: issues to do with communication (the starting point for providing any form of personal care), the skills and information you require in order to provide a higher quality care service and what further sources of assistance may be available to you.

All of what follows in this and in subsequent chapters must be considered in the context of the policies and practices of your employing organisation. A list of issues and topics upon which your organisation should have written guidance for your information is included in Appendix 2 of this book. If you have never been provided with this information – ask them for it. You need it!

Although you are generally working on your own, you should not be expected to work in a vacuum.

If you are self-employed you might like to think through these issues for yourself and, using *CareFully* as a guide, decide your own policies on these issues. This will then provide a consistent framework for your work with different people with different care needs.

BEFORE STARTING WORK WITH A NEW PERSON WITH CARE NEEDS

It is recognised that Home Care Assistants have a crucial part to play in the lives of people requiring care and their family and friends. Home Care Assistants are the ones most likely to be in frequent, regular contact with the person they are caring for. They may often become what is known as the 'keyworker', that is the main channel of contact and communication between the person receiving care, any designated 'care manager' they may have (responsible for developing the care plan and assessing care needs) and the organisation or agency commissioned or contracted to provide the care services. A three-way 'contract' is undertaken by all those involved.

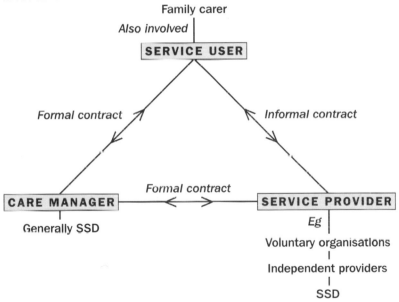

It is a sign of the importance of the Home Care Assistant's role that many employing organisations will now go to considerable lengths to try to 'match', as far as possible, the needs and personality of the person requiring care with those of the Home Care Assistant. It is becoming increasingly common for employing agencies to invite people needing care, and any family or personal carer they may have, to choose between two or three possible Home Care Assistants.

This is consistent with the desire to involve people receiving care in decisions relating to that care and to maximise their choice wherever possible.

This practice should increase and become more widespread. You should not be surprised, nor upset or offended, if you are not 'chosen' to be someone's Home Care Assistant. There is absolutely no point in inflicting contrasting personalities on one another, or you may be physically unsuited for the personal care tasks required. It is essential that the person receiving care and any family carer involved feel relaxed, secure and comfortable with the Home Care Assistant they have chosen.

Before starting work in someone's home you should have basic information about that person and their care needs. This may be extracted from their personal care plan or care assessment. If you do not have this basic information, ask your employing organisation for it.

You also need to know who else and what other agencies are also providing care services to that person. You may need to coordinate with them and schedule your visits to fit in with and meet the needs of the person you are caring for and their family carers. For example, it is not sensible for you to arrive at the same time that the district or community nurse comes to give the person a bath and the 'meals on wheels' are delivered. Besides the problem of everything happening at once, it does not help to break up the day for someone who may be housebound.

This is particularly important if the person is living alone and is confined to home. It will help reduce isolation if all those involved in providing care can visit on different days or at different times of the day. There is no point in everyone arriving at once. You will only get in one another's way and it will not help the person you are caring for.

You also need to be aware of what information the person has received. Do they have a copy of their own care plan? Do they have some form of contract or agreement with your employing organisation? What are their expectations of you and what you are going to do? Do they know what their rights are? Are they aware of the complaints procedure? Have any unmet needs been recorded and, if so, where?

There is a lot of basic information you require right from the start.

INTRODUCTION TO THE PERSON REQUIRING CARE AND TO THEIR FAMILY

It follows from what has already been written that your first entry into the home of the person you are going to care for should be planned and structured. You should not just turn up one morning and start work, hoping that everything will be all right.

However, regrettably, this does happen and it is to the credit of both the Home Care Assistant and the person being cared for that, in most cases, the arrangement works.

The initial stage of contact between the Home Care Assistant and the person with care needs is absolutely crucial because the success or otherwise of the first meetings will set the tone for the future of the relationship.

The process that should be followed is identified on the following page. It is often difficult, for many administrative and organisational reasons, for employing organisations to implement this process fully, but they should work towards it.

THE ROLE OF FAMILY CARERS

Family carers provide over 90 per cent of personal care. Home Care Assistants need to recognise the stress and personal pressure that family carers have experienced, often over periods of many years. They will continue to experience this most of the week when the Home Care Assistant is not present.

Pressures include not only the provision of care but also feelings of anxiety and guilt for many reasons, including not wanting or being able to provide all the care for themselves. Fatigue may be common, as a result of demanding caring responsibilities and probably sleepless nights. Many family carers are themselves older people and may themselves be infirm. If they are not, they are often juggling conflicting responsibilities such as child care and/or paid work.

The process of introducing the Home Care Assistant to the person needing care and their family

- The Home Care Assistant receives appropriate training and preparation before commencing work.

- The decision to provide care should be taken after assessment of care need, sometimes by staff from more than one agency (multi-disciplinary assessment).

- The person needing care should, wherever possible, be able to choose who becomes their Home Care Assistant.

- The Home Care Assistant should see the assessment of care that is required and/or the care plan, and know and understand and be able to discuss its objectives.

- The Home Care Assistant should be introduced to the person requiring care and their family and friends by someone from the agency with whom the person requiring care is familiar.

- The Home Care Assistant should be provided with some form of personal identification by their employing organisation.

- Care should be taken to ensure that everyone involved is completely clear about the role of the Home Care Assistant, the work and activities they will undertake and the level of personal care they will provide.

- The frequency with which the care will be provided must be known to all concerned, but it is sensible to retain a degree of flexibility to allow for sickness, holidays or other unforeseen events.

- Substitute arrangements to provide care in the Home Care Assistant's absence should be discussed and agreed in principle with all concerned.

- Measures for monitoring the quality of care provided and maintaining standards should be agreed by all concerned.

- There should be regular reviews of the care programme (or care package) at agreed times, to ensure that the care provided continues to meet the person's needs. The Home Care Assistant and the service user and family carers must be involved in the review.

- All concerned need to understand that, in spite of making every effort to give the person and their carers choice in the services that are provided, and listening to their views, there may be occasions when what the individual and the family want may not be what the caring agency can provide, nor what it thinks is appropriate.

As the Home Care Assistant you should show sympathy. Take care to not make any judgement about the way family carers have tried to cope in difficult circumstances. The working relationship should be one of partnership, where Home Care Assistants share the work with and relieve the family carers (for a very small part of the week at least).

The family carers know the person you are caring for, probably better than anyone else. They have acquired skills and expertise in caring for the person and there is much you can learn from them. For example, they have learnt from experience the best way to assist the person to take a bath, visit the toilet or eat their meals.

MATCHING WANTS, NEEDS AND THE PROVISION OF SERVICES

In spite of taking every effort in the early stages to clarify expectations and to involve the person being cared for and their family in all the decisions relating to the care, misunderstandings and differences of opinion do and will occur. Two examples will illustrate the point:

1   A person with care needs and their family place a high value on the cleanliness of the home. This is an important consideration, particularly where the person has been very houseproud. The care team/agency, although accepting the need for minimum standards of cleanliness, places the emphasis on the use of scarce home care time in providing physical care and in ensuring that vital shopping is done and money matters are dealt with. Whilst a compromise may be necessary, it is not always easy to achieve.

2   The need may be to provide care at times that are not covered by a personal family carer; for example, early mornings, late evenings, weekends (known as 'unsocial hours'). Although more flexible schemes are developing to meet these needs, it is not always possible to meet the exact requirements of the person and their family in this respect.

Can you think of other examples of differences of opinion and views between professionals, agencies providing care and the person receiving care and their family?

What was the outcome? Do you think that it was the right one in the circumstances?

These examples illustrate that you may sometimes find yourself working to two service users – the person with care needs and their personal family carer. You will need to discuss and clarify with both (separately and/or together) the tasks they are expecting to be done, how and in what order. It is not unknown for differences of opinion and even conflict to arise, and you may need considerable negotiating and mediating skills to reach agreement on exactly what both parties are expecting you to do.

THE IMPORTANCE OF GOOD COMMUNICATION

It is essential that you communicate well with the person you are caring for and their family from the very beginning of the relationship. Providing personal care, at whatever level, is an intimate activity. Somebody else is letting you, a comparative stranger, into their home and into their life.

Establishing good communication can often be quite difficult, particularly if the person you are caring for has some loss of hearing, speech or speech impairment and/or sight. It can take a while to get used to the fact that a person with poor sight does not respond to you visually, for example by smiling back at you or by making eye contact.

It is very possible that, at least initially, the person you are caring for may resent your presence. They may be mourning for their loss of independence. They may feel isolated and hurt and angry that they have become dependent on someone else to do things for them. This is an extremely common reaction and quite natural.

Think how you would feel in similar circumstances. Do you think you would react differently?

You need to respond with sensitivity and understanding at all times. You will need to learn when to be sympathetic and when to be firm. For example, people living on their own frequently 'open up' to Home Care Assistants, telling them their fears and anxieties and intimate details of their life. This requires sensitivity. On the other hand, some people are reluctant to do things for themselves if they think the Home Care Assistant can and will do it for them. That is the time to be firm!

A good starting point at the beginning of the relationship with the person you are caring for and their family is to introduce yourself, saying what name they should call you by and asking them how they would like you to address them.

You should never make assumptions about this, nor call people by their first names unless specifically invited to do so. Many older people and people from some ethnic minority communities do not like anyone other than family or intimate friends calling them by their first name. It is a sign of disrespect to do so. Other good practice in communication includes:

- talking directly to the person face to face;
- making eye contact;
- speaking clearly – pronouncing words clearly and not talking too fast;
- using touch appropriately, for example to gain their attention, but not over-familiarly;
- if the person cannot see, or has poor sight, saying who you are immediately upon arrival, explaining what you are doing while you are working and telling the person when you are leaving or entering a room;
- clearly listening to the person, their problems, life history, etc;
- trying to avoid personal mannerisms (eg the use of terms such as 'love', 'pet' or 'dear') before you know for certain that they will not offend.

Poor practice in communication that should always be avoided includes:

- talking too loud or shouting to make people hear and understand;
- talking too slowly;
- talking 'down' to people as if they are children;
- adopting a superficial approach (eg 'there, there, dear, it will all come out in the wash') or artificial jollity;
- over-correcting the person and unnecessary contradiction;
- showing impatience rather than listening.

Think about how you communicate with people – do you automatically adopt the good practices identified above or do you find yourself using any of the examples of poor practice?

YOUR NEEDS AS THE HOME CARE ASSISTANT

Your contribution as the Home Care Assistant is essential to the success of any programme of care provided for vulnerable people.

As has already been identified, the Home Care Assistant is most often the 'keyworker', that is to say the person who is most frequently in contact with the person requiring care and knows more about them and their care needs than anyone else within the care agencies.

Organisations providing care overlook the views and needs of the Home Care Assistant at their peril.

The Home Care Assistant should be provided with, or have access to, the following, through their employing agency:

- Induction training upon appointment and regular refresher training thereafter.
- Basic training through the National Vocational Qualification (NVQ) system (the Integrated Care awards), to develop competence in the work.
- Support, for example from other Home Care Assistants and from workers from other agencies carrying out similar or complementary tasks.
- Regular, structured supervision from immediate supervisor/manager/ organiser (unless registered self-employed).
- A system of obtaining help in an emergency.
- A system of obtaining help and advice at any other time.
- Colleagues and managers at work who will listen to them and take their views and opinions into account and recognise the stress that occurs in the work.
- Managers who value them and their work, monitor their progress and give them feedback on their performance.

Is there anything you would add to this list?

In Appendices 2 and 5 of this book is further information that should be provided for Home Care Assistants, on the organisation's policies and practices and on training. Unless you are self-employed, you should also have a contract of employment and a job description.

SOURCES OF ASSISTANCE

As well as the help that can be expected from your own agency, it is also good practice to draw up a list together with the person you are caring for and their family and friends, of other sources of help, such as those identified in the following checklist. This should be done when you first begin work with a new person receiving services.

Not all the information will be either available or required but you should be able to obtain the essential details (see pp 38–39).

This list should be kept in a prominent place, with the agreement of the person concerned, for ease of reference; for example, by the telephone or by the front or back door.

It would be very easy for your care agency to provide you and all your colleague Home Care Assistants with a printed list that could be filled in. If you do not have one already, why not suggest it to them? The list should also be available in the appropriate format for the individual person; for example, in the language generally used by that person or in large type or braille for people who are partially sighted.

Very often the actual existence and details of such sources of assistance can help the person needing care and their family to feel more secure – not to mention the Home Care Assistant!

You will also need to be aware of national and local voluntary organisations that provide services and/or equipment. The list of organisations and their addresses in Appendix 7 is a starting point.

CASE STUDY – A DAY IN THE LIFE OF A FAMILY CARER

Morning Start at 7 am with a call from Mother to use the commode.

Remove my bedding and mattress from the hall. (I sleep here in order to avoid falling on the stairs in the night when attending to Mother.)

Help Mother to wash, dress and get her to walk to the front room with the aid of a Zimmer frame.

Get some breakfast for us both.

Mother then needs to use the commode again.

Wash and dress myself.

Make Mother's bed, air the room, empty the commode, etc.

Wash Mother's soiled clothing and make sure of sufficient dry clothing for the next day – or the next time needed – possibly the same day.

Mother will then need to use the commode again.

This happens about every 2 hours. As she cannot get out of the chair without help and dare not let go of the Zimmer in case she falls down, she has to be attended and toileted the whole time. This is quite a time-consuming operation.

I then make hot drinks and a light lunch for us both.

Afternoon I either do housework or a little tidying up in the garden, or go to local shops for necessities or into town to pick up incontinence supplies.

Make tea for us both and try to get Mother to peel potatoes and carrots while I prepare and cook the evening meal.

Evening After the meal, wash up while Mother falls asleep in front of TV.

I fall asleep myself the moment I sit down because the only time I have sat down all day was to eat.

When Mother wakes because of a quiet spell on TV, I make moves to get her to bed.

Prepare her room for easy access during the night.

Make up my own bed on the hall floor and try to get some sleep before the broken night begins.

Questions

1   *How would you feel in the above situation? How long do you think you could cope in this situation?*

2   *What emotions and feelings do you think the carer is experiencing?*

3   *What help do you think the carer needs?*

KEY POINTS

- The Home Care Assistant is of vital importance in the life of the person being cared for, as the person most frequently in regular contact (keyworker).

- People needing care will increasingly be involved in decisions on who becomes their Home Care Assistant, and will be given a choice.

- The Home Care Assistant must have detailed information of the care plan or the assessed need and know who else is involved in providing care.

- The initial introduction of the Home Care Assistant into the home must be planned and structured.

- It is important to involve service users and their family carers in decisions relating to their care, and enable them to contribute to the care plan and clarify expectations.

- The importance of effective communication between the Home Care Assistant and the person needing care and their family carer must not be overlooked.

- The Home Care Assistant must always respond with sensitivity and understanding to the needs of the person they are caring for, and separately to the particular needs of the family carer.

- Employing organisations and agencies must provide Home Care Assistants with support and basic information on policies and practices, in order to enable them to provide a high-quality service. This cannot be achieved in a vacuum.

- A list of key telephone numbers should be kept in a prominent place in the home of each person receiving care.

Other sources of help

Names, addresses, telephone numbers of:

Family & relatives

Close friends

General practitioner

Care manager/keyworker

Religious leader

Dentist

Chiropodist

Hairdresser

District nurse

Community psychiatric nurse

Solicitor

Welfare rights adviser

Social Security office

Social Service office

Voluntary organisations &
support groups

Day centres

Local branch of Age Concern

3 The Basic Skills of Home Care Assistants

This chapter explores the issues involved in starting to work in someone else's home. It looks at whose standards should be applied and goes on to discuss some of the basic activities that the Home Care Assistant undertakes.

In order to avoid repetition, some activities are covered more fully in subsequent chapters (eg providing meals and helping with eating and drinking). This chapter includes some specific issues in relation to providing care to people from ethnic minority communities.

STARTING WORK

You must always remember that when you enter the home of a person who needs care, you do so at their invitation. An invitation that they have the right to withdraw at any time. There is absolutely no obligation on anyone at any time to accept a service that they may need but which they do not want.

You should always be very aware that you are working in someone else's home – not your own – and treat it accordingly.

Only 15 years ago, the main argument against introducing training for Home Care Assistants was that 'they are only doing in someone else's home what they would do in their own'. Today we recognise that that is not true. Every home, person and situation is different and all Home Care Assistants need training in order to respond appropriately.

You should be clear, before entering the person's home, about the caring tasks you are expected to do. Your employing organisation should identify and inform you of tasks you should not undertake. These are generally because they represent a health and safety hazard to you, the Home Care Assistant, and/or the person you are caring for (see later in this chapter and in Chapter 6 on 'Health and Safety'). The sorts of tasks involved include lifting heavy objects, moving heavy furniture, any activity that involves standing on ladders, etc. If in doubt, ask your agency or employing organisation.

The tasks you do should have been agreed and clarified in advance between the person needing care, their personal or family carer, and the person putting together the care plan or the care package. If, when you arrive, you find that there is any difference in opinion or expectation about the work you will do, this should be reported immediately to your line manager, who may be in a position to advise who could undertake those tasks that you are either not allowed or not required to do yourself.

However, you should take care to establish from the very beginning exactly how each person wishes you to undertake each task and their personal preferences.

The home and all its possessions must always be treated with respect and objects handled with care. Accidents can and will happen, as everyone recognises, but care should be taken to prevent them occurring, if at all possible. If the person has poor vision and is unable to see clearly, avoid moving objects and furniture from their usual place.

Unless specifically asked to find a personal document or possession, you should never look through private papers or personal belongings.

When in someone else's home you should not make yourself a cup of tea or coffee, help yourself to biscuits, etc, unless you are invited to do so. Many employers do not allow their Home Care Assistants to smoke while on duty. Even if it is not a policy of your particular agency, it is certainly **good practice** not to smoke.

Above all, you should always remember that you are there to assist the person remain in their own home. This means supporting and maintaining their independence as far as possible. You should therefore always encourage the person to do as much as possible for themselves and never do things for them that they could do for themselves.

Agree on certain tasks that can be left for the person to carry out themselves, taking into account their degree of disability. Encourage them to undertake tasks *with* you if possible and involve them in the running of the home. Avoid increasing their dependence.

WHOSE STANDARDS?

Whose standards should apply? Yours, or those relating to the person receiving care? Very few people have exactly the same standards and you must be open-minded and flexible. Above all, you should never try to impose your standards on others. What is considered a nice, tidy, comfortable home to one person may be a cold, unfriendly and impersonal place to another or a hopeless muddle to a third.

Your aim is to enable each individual person to lead as normal a life as possible within their normal surroundings. You therefore, within reason, assume their standards.

This does not necessarily mean that you cannot make certain changes such as moving furniture, washing crockery, throwing away papers and food, etc but only with the complete permission of the person you are caring for.

Hygiene standards can also be an area of concern. This is an issue that is picked up under the next section, on 'Health and Safety'.

How would you describe your own personal standards? How do you think that these may relate to or affect the people you are caring for? How do you think you really feel about other people's standards?

HEALTH AND SAFETY

You must always take account of health and safety in your work. Both your health and safety and those of the person you are caring for. Most employing organisations have policies relating to health and safety as a result of the Health and Safety at Work etc Act 1974, which is now amended by the European Directive on Manual Handling (90/269/EEC). Information on these policies should be part of your induction training.

Check up on the policies and find out what you can and cannot do. Most organisations have some regulations relating to (for example) not climbing ladders.

Before you start work in the home, it should have been checked by your line manager or some other person for any particular health and safety problems. Find out about the results of the check before you enter the home.

In some homes factors such as poor lighting, cluttered furniture and worn or frayed carpets can represent safety hazards to the person living in the home and everyone who visits it. In these situations you can only advise the person or their family to make changes and try gentle persuasion! If you are seriously concerned about a hazard, report it to your line manager.

Hygiene is also part of health and safety and can be quite a problem in the provision of home care services, as standards can vary so considerably. In general, it is always important that you keep the toilet and bathroom clean as well as the kitchen areas where food is prepared, to prevent the risk of infection.

Many employers provide Home Care Assistants with some form of protective clothing to wear while working. Most, if not all, issue protective gloves in order to protect both the service user and the Home Care Assistant while carrying out personal care tasks.

Much more information on health and safety may be found in Chapter 6.

BASIC CARE ACTIVITIES

You as the Home Care Assistant will be required to carry out a number of important and often personal or intimate services for the person you are caring for.

The following guidance describes the principal basic care activities undertaken by the Home Care Assistant, with particular reference to the need for sensitivity and flexibility.

Further information on some of these tasks may be found in the relevant chapters of this book.

Helping people to get out of bed

If one of your tasks is to help people to get up, make certain that any routine is flexible; some older people will wish to get up immediately upon waking; others will need time to prepare themselves. Where possible, the time of each morning visit should take into account the wishes and preferences of the person you are assisting.

Always knock before entering the room, and wait to be invited in – don't walk in at the same time as you knock! Open the door slowly so as not to startle the person. This is particularly important if they have difficulty hearing and may not have heard your knock.

Ask if they are ready to get up. If they are not, and there is no urgent reason for them to do so, attend to other tasks until they wish to get up. However, the gap between the first greeting and returning to assist with getting up should not be longer than about a quarter of an hour, particularly where attempts to get out of bed unaided could lead to a fall.

Talk to the person about the day ahead and what they are going to do in a way that is relevant to them, bearing in mind their circumstances and lifestyle.

Assist the person to the toilet or commode if necessary.

Keep alert for any signs of incontinence, illness or injury, such as difficulty with breathing, coughing, bruising, weakness of upper limbs, numbness. Always enquire very sensitively about any such signs in order not to alarm the person you are caring for.

Dressing and undressing

Always respect the person's privacy and dignity at all times. There is no need to stay in the room if the person is able to dress or partially dress themselves. You should encourage as much independence in dressing and undressing as possible.

Always let the person choose for themselves what they wish to wear – it enhances their self-esteem. However, you may need to assist someone with poor sight or visual disability to match colours.

You need to be conscious of, and sensitive to, the frustration that can be generated by weakness and loss of ability. Offer help sympathetically;

allow plenty of time, taking into account any illness, physical impairment or disability. A positive attitude is more likely to encourage an interest in personal appearance.

You will need to know exactly what help each person needs and that a particular method of dressing might be necessary; for example, someone who has suffered a stroke might be unaware of their affected side. Simple aids may also assist the person to dress themselves (eg something to help pull up a zip on the back of a dress). The advice of the occupational therapist can always be sought to help you help the people you are caring for.

Some people may find it easier to dress themselves if clothes are laid out. Clothes should be selected in advance to ensure that a person is never left undressed while a new set of clothes is sought.

Washing, shaving and dental care

Most people wish to continue to look after their personal hygiene themselves for as long as possible, and you should do everything to encourage this.

Some people, however, may need reminding tactfully and you may have to assist with the everyday tasks of washing, shaving and looking after their hair and teeth.

For most people, their self-respect is enhanced when they feel clean and comfortable. There should be emphasis on:

■ Regular washing of hands and face.

■ Regular combing of hair.

■ For men without a beard, regular shaving at a frequency best suited to the needs of the individual (an electric razor may allow them to do it for themselves).

■ Regular cleaning of teeth or dentures.

■ Cleaning of spectacles.

NOTE Nail trimming should always be carried out by an appropriately qualified person or by a district nurse or chiropodist. Don't try to do it yourself – particularly if you do not have the qualifications. Some voluntary organisations, including some local Age Concern groups, will trim nails.

Bathing

Taking a bath does not have to be a regular routine, and a person's preference in this matter is likely to be determined by the habits of a lifetime.

The time of a bath should be arranged taking this into consideration. Bathing should be a pleasant experience which is enjoyed. Some people may prefer a strip wash or a shower.

Whenever possible, people should be encouraged to bath themselves. However, they may feel more secure taking a bath when someone else is in the home, in case anything goes wrong or they fall. Or they may wish assistance in and out of the bath, particularly if it has high sides.

Where possible, assistance with bathing should be carried out by the regular carer. Always check the temperature of the water before allowing the person to use the bath. Dipping the elbow in is the traditional and easy way of doing this.

Always allow the person time for a relaxing and therapeutic soak. Check for any obvious signs of illness or disability, sensitively. If possible, leave the person alone in the bathroom for a while, if necessary remaining within earshot in case help is needed.

In accordance with lifting and handling regulations (see Chapter 6), if the person actually requires lifting into or out of the bath, equipment such as a hoist should be made available. Never try to lift the person yourself, even if there are two of you. You could hurt the person you are assisting, as well as damage yourself.

If you need to assist by providing a steady hand and support, be sensitive to the intimacy of the situation and recognise that the person may be embarrassed. Remember their rights to privacy, dignity and respect, identified in Chapter 1.

As an alternative to a bath, encourage the person to take a shower or have a strip wash.

Sometimes some people forget to wash or bathe and may not recognise that they need to do so for hygienic reasons. A simple but tactful reminder may be enough.

Refusal to bathe may be for various sensitive reasons such as embarrassment that physical help is needed and they can't do it for themselves, the threat of being touched, shame about incontinence, or the desire to hide the evidence of incontinence.

The advice of an occupational therapist or district nurse may be sought concerning the availability of bath aids. In some situations, the installation of a shower can enable people to bathe unaided when they couldn't manage the bath.

Assisting with meals

Eating can be one of life's pleasures, and a social activity. Meal times should be looked forward to, and time should be spent with people while they eat.

When shopping, make sure some foods that require no preparation, such as bread, cheese, cold meats, fruit and breakfast cereals, are bought so that the person you are caring for can get their own meals with ease.

If one of your tasks is to prepare a person's meal – breakfast, lunch or supper – where possible, it should be provided at a time which suits that person, encouraging them to take part in choosing the menu.

Always allow plenty of time for eating meals and avoid rushing.

Care should be taken to lay the table or tray attractively, ensuring that food looks appetising on the plate. If the person is confused, it may be necessary to ensure that they eat the meal you have prepared.

Further information may be found in Chapter 5.

Shopping

If shopping is undertaken, it is important to remember to encourage the person's independence and participation in the process.

Whenever possible, take the person with you. This not only gives the individual the chance to get out of the house but also allows them to choose the items they want and to see what else is available.

If the person has a sight problem, you should ask them how they would like you to escort them. Some people may prefer to take your arm, in which case you should walk slightly ahead of them and indicate when you get to kerbs. In shops you will need to read out labels and prices and – most helpfully – spot the special offers!

If it is not possible to take the person with you, try to involve them in preparing and preferably writing a detailed shopping list, which identifies not only what they want but also where it should be bought – if possible.

When handling cash or cheques, it is important to go through it clearly with the individual; for example, 'I have taken a £10 note out of your purse for the shopping today'. It may help to write it down in a cash book which can be readily referred to if a query arises. Always obtain a receipt for any goods purchased so that you can account for any money taken. (This is picked up again in Chapter 10.)

An awareness of the problems older people face when trying to eat healthily is necessary; it may be important on occasions to be able to give advice on budgeting for healthy eating. This is followed up in Chapter 5.

When putting the shopping away, ensure that food is stored correctly, and always in accordance with the instructions on the packaging. Most people with poor sight will have their own system for keeping certain types of food in particular places. If possible, the person should put the food away themselves as you read out the labels.

Always take care when handling food. Remember to wash your hands before touching food and to use clean containers and utensils.

Remember that medicines and household cleaning agents that you have bought are potentially dangerous; care should therefore be taken with the storage, handling and disposal of such items. Again this is particularly important for people with poor sight. Medicines must be clearly identifiable. This may be done by using a special shape of container or labelling in large print or braille.

Going to bed

If you are responsible for helping to put someone to bed, remember that everyone likes to go to bed when it suits them. They may have long established bed-time routines, which must be respected.

- Establish exactly what help is needed at bed time.
- Avoid hustling and hurrying.
- Be prepared to be patient.

- As already identified, many people will be able to look after their own personal hygiene but they may need some encouragement. Use good humour and gentle persuasion.

- If the person you are caring for does need help with their personal hygiene, remember to protect their dignity and self-respect at all times.

- If you are providing care for someone who is suffering from incontinence, it is imperative to ensure that good clean skin care practices are followed, regularly washing your hands with soap.

- Be particularly sensitive to any action that might cause embarrassment.

- Seek ways of involving the person you are caring for and gaining their cooperation in whatever care and support must be provided.

- Maintain the person's privacy at all times.

LEAVING THE HOME

Check at the end of each visit that tasks have been carried out satisfactorily.

When leaving the home, ensure that the person is comfortable and that everything necessary is within easy reach; for example, a drink, medication, newspapers, access to the commode.

However, if the person is confused, it may be necessary to ensure that any potential sources of danger are not too accessible – put away medication, switch off the cooker and other appliances, etc.

Make sure that the home is secure. If leaving during the day, check that the person knows which windows are open (if any) and that they or someone else will be able to close them at the end of the day. It may be necessary to leave some lights on if the person is not readily mobile and there will be no further visitors before it begins to get dark.

Close the door securely, locking any locks necessary.

CARING FOR PEOPLE FROM ETHNIC MINORITY COMMUNITIES

The attitude and approach towards the provision of care recommended in this book should apply equally to people of all cultures. However, people from ethnic minority communities have specific needs which may not be met in the most sensitive and appropriate way if they are treated exactly the same as people from white European cultures.

You should never be expected to provide care in their own homes, to people from ethnic minority communities, without first completing an appropriate training course. There is far more you need to learn about cultural and religious beliefs and differences, and about your own attitudes, than could possibly be included in this book.

We can, however, begin to highlight some issues. In order to ensure that people needing care who belong to ethnic minority communities get the same services as others, special attention should be paid to the following points.

Language

For many people from ethnic minority communities, English is not their first language. Never assume an understanding of what a person may be saying; for example, someone being 'difficult' about eating their food may be trying to indicate that the food is contrary to their religion or that they are diabetic. Older people from ethnic minority communities may not understand English. If you find yourself working in this situation, it would show sensitivity to try to learn a few key words in the relevant language.

Has the person needing care been given information, for example the care plan or the complaints procedure, in their own language? If not, how much are they really able to understand about the process, what they are entitled to, what you are able to help with, etc? How confusing do you think it is, not to have information in your own language?

Interpreters

Whenever difficulties occur, and always for the first meeting, an interpreter should be used. (It is not permissible to use children for this.) Some areas have an interpreting service, or the local community relations council may help.

Culture

You need to understand about significant religious days; for example, Diwali (Festival of Light) is important to Sikhs and Hindus, and Ramadan to Muslims, just as Easter is to Christians.

Service provision

Whenever appropriate and possible, Home Care Assistants should be recruited from within the same ethnic community as the person needing care. Unfortunately, this is not always possible. You may therefore need to be aware of particular needs; for example, Muslims always wash plates and crockery under running water to avoid contamination.

Provision of food

Particular note should be taken of religious and cultural preferences so that the appropriate diet is observed. In cultures where it is normal to eat with the fingers, the usual feeding aids and utensils will not be required.

Clothes

You will need to know how to assist people with the clothes of their choice and understand what is correct for the occasion and time of day. The local community relations council or religious centre (eg the local temple) can offer advice.

SPECIALIST CARE SCHEMES

Many home care agencies now offer specific services to meet particular needs. For example:

- Night sitting service when a person needs someone in attendance at night.
- Discharge from hospital – a more intensive service for people who have been discharged early or need to ease the move from hospital to home.
- Out of hours service for people who need care early morning, at night or at weekends.
- Respite service – generally 24 hours to give the personal family carer a break.

If you are not directly involved in these specialist schemes yourself, find out which schemes operate in your area, so that you can give advice if necessary.

ENABLING PERSONAL CHOICE

It is the right of the individual being cared for to be listened to, to have their views respected and to have their wishes and opinions taken into consideration (see Chapter 1). This is of great importance. However, the individual's wishes can, on occasion, conflict with the 'professional' opinion about what is actually in their best interest.

You as the Home Care Assistant can be caught in the middle. For example:

1   A person with bronchitis and emphysema who has smoked for 60 years might be encouraged to stop smoking (the professional view). The person may reject such advice and their decision must be respected.

2   An older person may become forgetful, but yet insist on carrying out cooking and other activities in which there is a significant element of risk that they may harm themselves. A compromise may be possible with high-risk activities being undertaken under supervision by the Home Care Assistant.

3   A person may be substantially overweight, with the resulting problems of mobility and weight-related diseases. The professional view might seek to impose diet and exercise. The individual may prefer to continue as they are. Persuasion may be tried and might be at least partially effective with some people. If not, the views and wishes of the individual concerned must prevail.

In general:

- Respect the right of the individual to **choose**.
- Try to change behaviour that could possibly be harmful and/or dangerous, by the use of **reasoning** and **persuasion**.
- Seek to achieve an acceptable **balance** between the professional view and wishes and those of the person concerned. This may not be easy!

- Wherever possible, seek to encourage, stimulate and maintain the **independence** of the person needing care.
- **Don't** encourage unnecessary or premature dependence.
- Keep the person's family and friends informed of what you are trying to do and why. **Involve** and **consult** them whenever possible and appropriate.

INFORMING ON MATTERS OF SERIOUS CONCERN

This is sometimes known as 'whistleblowing'!

You will find that, in time, you as a Home Care Assistant will often know more about the person you are caring for than anyone else. Sometimes you may find yourself in the position of becoming aware of unacceptable or even criminal practices involving the person and undertaken by others including, for example, members of the family, friends, other carers.

This may include (for example):

- physical/sexual abuse;
- mental cruelty;
- theft (money, jewellery, antiques, furniture);
- coercion (to change Will, enter residential home, etc).

Your first duty as a Home Care Assistant in these circumstances is to protect the person you are caring for. Any practices that may involve any of the above and/or the possibility of risk to the individual concerned must be reported at once to your line manager.

AND FINALLY

It is important that as a Home Care Assistant you recognise the need to be always aware that the level of care and assistance provided should reflect the actual needs of the person being cared for.

It is quite common for a physically and/or mentally frail person to initially need a considerable amount of intensive care, but it may be possible to reduce the level of such assistance if there is an improvement in their condition. A person with sight problems who is receiving rehabilitation training will gradually require less care.

On the other hand, someone who is relatively 'fit and able' can be provided with too much care, resulting in increased dependency rather than increased independence.

It cannot be over-emphasised – as was said at the beginning of this chapter – that all tasks should be undertaken, wherever possible, with the aim of stimulating and encouraging people to do as much as possible for themselves and increasing their independence.

The degree to which dependency is being unintentionally created can be difficult to determine, particularly if you have not worked as a Home Care Assistant for any significant length of time.

This is an issue that should be covered in your initial training and supervision and in the monitoring and care review sessions relating to the effectiveness of the total care package for each person.

Always remember that your responsibility as a Home Care Assistant is not to create or reinforce dependency. You should seek to provide the level of care that is determined by the condition of the person and to vary the level of care to reflect changes in that condition.

CASE STUDY

Mr T, aged 87, lived alone in a terraced house in a big city. He coped quite well, with some help from friends and neighbours and a visit from a Home Care Assistant once a week. He was a proud independent man who liked his home and was determined to stay in it.

For some years he had had circulation problems, affecting particularly his legs and feet. This condition got worse to the point where he had to be admitted to hospital for the amputation of both his legs at the knee. He was in hospital for 12 weeks and, upon discharge, insisted on returning home.

Rehabilitation had been started in hospital, and when he arrived home he was provided with intensive care carried out on a daily basis by two Home

Care Assistants and a district nurse. Some basic adaptations were made to his house to enable him to use a wheelchair and to provide access to the upstairs bedroom and bathroom/toilet.

The rehabilitation was continued by carers, health service staff, friends and neighbours. Care over all was intensive and was aimed at assisting and encouraging Mr T towards self-sufficiency. Within three months he had much improved; it was possible to reduce levels of care so that he was maintained by a Home Care Assistant visiting three times a week and by the continuing daily help from friends.

Mr T stayed in his house for over a year and it was his decision eventually to move to a flat because two of his friends were moving there.

Despite a serious operation late in his life, Mr T was able, with intensive help, to maintain a good quality of life and to exercise his choice over what happened to him.

Questions

1   *What individual skills do you think the Home Care Assistants used in caring for Mr T?*

2   *What was the aim of the care provided by the agencies and Mr T's friends?*

3   *Would it have been easier and more 'cost effective' to have kept Mr T in hospital or in a nursing home?*

KEY POINTS

- Never forget that you are working in someone else's home and treat it accordingly.
- You must always encourage the people you are caring for to do as much as possible for themselves to sustain their independence and enable them to remain in their own homes.
- Never impose your own personal standards; within reason, assume those of the people you are caring for.
- You need to take account of health and safe working practices for your own sake, as well as that of the people you are caring for.
- Basic care tasks should always be undertaken flexibly and with sensitivity.

- When encouraging people to do things for themselves, allow them all the time they need. Never rush or hurry them.

- Always respect the right of the individual to choose; use persuasion to change potentially harmful behaviour.

- Never assume that everyone is the same – we are all different. You will need appropriate training before working with people from ethnic minority communities with care needs.

- Always keep the person, their family and friends fully informed on what you are doing. Your duty is to protect the people you are caring for. If you suspect they are being exploited in any way by their family and friends (eg physical abuse), report it at once.

Summary of good caring skills

- Listening to people and what they have to say.

- Observing people and recognising when their needs change.

- Using patience, tact and persuasion.

- Avoiding confrontation.

- Recognising people's fears and frustrations.

- Putting people at ease.

- Respecting people's rights to privacy, dignity and self-respect.

- Giving essential care with gentleness, tact and confidence.

- Causing minimum discomfort.

- Recognising when to seek help from others.

- Providing care *with* people rather than *for* them.

4 The Health of Older People

Many of the people you will care for in their own homes will be in need of care because they are mentally and/or physically frail. This applies particularly to older people, who tend to become more susceptible to illness the longer they live. This chapter introduces you to the ageing process and to some of the more common illnesses of later life. It discusses ways of maintaining the health of the older person, including the need for social and emotional care. The chapter also explores particular issues in relation to medication and caring for people who are aggressive or refuse to care for themselves.

CHANGES IN THE BODY AND COMMON PROBLEMS

The changes described below are due partly to ageing and partly to disease. Being old does not make a person ill or disabled. Even when ageing is partly responsible for a problem, treatment may still be possible. Older people are as entitled to benefit from health care and social services as younger people are. Try to encourage your older clients to seek help for health problems, and not to think these are 'just old age'.

As the body ages:

- The skin becomes drier and more wrinkled, and brown spots may appear on the backs of the hands. Finger and toenails thicken and get more brittle. Hair becomes grey and thins; early greying and baldness run in families. People may 'shrink', becoming shorter, because the discs between the vertebrae become thinner and also because of bone changes.

- Bones become thinner and more brittle (osteoporosis) and may also lose calcium; they therefore break more easily. Softened vertebrae may be crushed by the weight they carry. This painful process bends the spine, so the person becomes stooped. Bone changes happen much faster in women than in men, but can be slowed down by hormone replacement therapy.

- Muscles become less powerful and joints less supple. These changes can be much less in people who keep active and take exercise. Inactive old people become progressively less and less mobile.

- Balance and coordination deteriorate with age. This can make older people more likely to fall over, especially if they have health problems or the home is unsafe.

- Older people are at risk from extremes of temperature because their body's temperature-control mechanisms become less efficient.

- Hearing may be impaired, especially with group conversations, in noisy surroundings or when speech is distorted (eg by a public address system in railway station announcements). Hearing-impaired people may be thought to be confused if their hearing problem is not identified. Treatment or a hearing aid may help.

- As the lens of the eye loses focusing power, spectacles become necessary for close work such as reading; this is quite normal. However, two out of five people over 75 years old have sight problems affecting their independence and enjoyment of life. This is abnormal and should be investigated. Common causes are cataracts, macular degeneration, glaucoma and diabetes. Treatment can prevent or halt sight loss; in addition, the affected person can be helped to make the most of their remaining sight.

- Taste and smell become less acute. This may reduce the older person's enjoyment of food.

- Teeth may be lost because of gum disease, and dentures work loose as gums shrink. Good dental care with frequent check-ups can keep teeth healthy for life. People with dentures should have them checked once a year.

- Incontinence of urine and/or stool can develop. This is not due to ageing alone, and it can often be successfully treated.
- Older people often suffer from constipation. Fibre in the diet, plenty of fluids and adequate exercise can prevent this.
- The lungs and airways become less efficient. Heart and blood vessel disease becomes more common and blood pressure tends to rise. Older people are more likely to suffer from strokes, chest infections, arthritis, diabetes and cancer than younger people are.

Remember that no one older person will suffer from all or even most of these conditions.

Never assume that getting older automatically makes someone disabled or ill.

Always treat people according to their condition and not according to their age.

Think about some of the older people you know. How many would you consider to be fit and active? How many would you describe as being 'young in spirit'. Now think about some younger people. Would you describe any of these as being 'old before their time'? Why do you think this has happened?

We can therefore make some important points about the ageing process that you should keep in mind:

- People can age at different rates. Some people in their 70s can appear to be in their 50s, and vice versa.
- Never assume that an older person can't improve, both mentally and physically.
- A healthy life-style can prevent or delay some of the illnesses that can affect older people. The most important thing is not to smoke; it is never too late for a person's health to benefit from giving up. Regular exercise helps to keep older people active. Eating a good variety of foods, with plenty of fibre, fruit and vegetables, and fluids also helps. The possible link between animal fats and heart disease is less important in later life.
- Never equate old age with ill health or disabilities. If you treat older people as if they are ill, they may respond by letting you do everything for them, and so losing the ability to do whatever they can for themselves. The majority of people aged over 70 are very fit and active. However, they

are unlikely to be receiving home care services. The people you care for will be frailer than average and not typical of older people as a group.

- Do not patronise or 'talk down' to adults about their health or disabilities. Phrases such as 'How are we today then?' should be avoided, however kindly they are meant.

- Maintain strict confidentiality about what you know about a person's medical condition, or, for that matter, about anything else you might know about him or her. The only exception to the rule is when you may need to report to a GP, district nurse or other health professional, including your line manager, on any matters that concern the person receiving care.

Keep in mind that people should **never** be described as if they were illnesses. People are not 'diabetics', 'epileptics' or 'schizophrenics.' They are *people* with diabetes, epilepsy or schizophrenia. The emphasis must always be on the person, not on the illness.

Appendix 6 lists the more common illnesses and disabilities that may affect older people. Some of these conditions are preventable, whilst others can improve or be kept stable with proper care. Some are progressive, and then treatment aims to keep the sufferer as comfortable as possible. The aim of care is to keep people in good health and to make sure that any disabilities interfere with their lives as little as possible.

SOCIAL AND EMOTIONAL CARE

Personal care becomes superficial if the sole concern is for physical needs. In order to maintain the health of the older person you must take into account their social and emotional needs as well as their physical needs. This is known as caring for 'the whole person' and in practice all three – physical, social and emotional care – cannot be separated. The provision of physical care can be an excellent opportunity to establish a rapport with the person you are caring for, and develop trust.

It is important to get to know the people you are caring for as individuals, their likes and dislikes, their skills, interests and experiences. You can be an important link in helping them to retain contact with people and activities outside of their home.

In Chapter 2 we looked at the importance of effective communication in establishing a relationship with the person you are caring for. Good communication is the vital ingredient in meeting people's social and emotional needs.

Conversation with the person receiving care is just as important in maintaining their health and their morale as undertaking the physical tasks. It is important that you spend time talking to the person you are caring for, and building up a relationship. They may be suffering from a sense of loss from a recent bereavement and need to talk about it. Be sympathetic and understanding. One of the worst things that can happen is if a bereaved person is not allowed to talk about the loss of a loved one and they have to 'bottle' it up inside themselves when really it would be better if they were encouraged to share it with you, the Home Care Assistant. Helping people talk about their feelings is important.

Reminiscing about the past is another natural and healthy activity and is often used as a means of reorientating people who show signs of confusion. There is much of interest to be learned from the life experiences of an older person.

However, do not assume that older people have no interest in matters of today. A lively interest in current affairs should be encouraged. Older people particularly may experience the loss of involvement in the world, and a general feeling of isolation and being unable to participate. Bringing in a newspaper and discussing what is happening can help reduce their sense of isolation.

Loneliness and isolation is a major problem for many people needing care, and also for any personal family carers there may be. For many people, you, the Home Care Assistant, will be the only regular visitor. Loneliness may be made worse by a sense of loss – not only of a loved one but also loss of health, loss of a way of life, loss of independence.

Some people are simply wishing away their time. For them, each day is a burden to be borne as best they can. It is important that the work of caring includes the understanding and acceptance of such feelings. They are very real, and time should be allowed for them to be expressed and explored, and for you to try to know and respect each person as an individual.

Helping to overcome loneliness and loss is vital. People become withdrawn, sleepy, depressed and anxious. Frequently they have problems sleeping and a decreased appetite. Severe depression can often be treated by medication or counselling. The Home Care Assistant is in an ideal position to recognise these symptoms and take appropriate action to alleviate them, including reporting to the line manager, GP or district nurse.

It is essential that time and energy are spent trying to improve the value and quality of a person's life. It is worth stressing that, no matter how dependent and frail a person may become, day activities and a social life should be considered as part of their general health and well-being. Regularly ask questions such as: 'Is there anything that you would particularly like to do today?' Maybe with help some things can be achieved. Where this is not possible, perhaps the opportunity to talk about 'What I would do if only . . .' would ease the frustration of knowing what is impossible now.

People may become housebound not because they are immobile but because of disabilities such as poor sight. Apart from their difficulty in getting about, people with a visual handicap may lack information about local activities because they are unable to read newspapers, etc. You can help overcome these difficulties by telling them about events and finding ways of helping them get out, perhaps with the assistance of volunteers.

Action you can take to reduce social and emotional isolation includes:

- Discover each person's special interests.
- Try to encourage activities that are related to past pleasures.
- Assist in the writing of letters, making telephone calls, arranging visits.
- Discover whether assistance is required to continue lifelong hobbies.
- Encourage relatives, friends, visitors, outings and general contact with the outside world.
- Seek the involvement of the local community and voluntary organisations wherever possible.
- Religious beliefs may have been significant in the person's life. Where possible, help them to continue participating in meetings, services, ceremonies, etc, or ask the appropriate religious leader to visit.
- Aids are available to help with activities; for example, large print books, craft materials and talking books (audio tapes).
- Many areas of the country are served by mobile libraries which enable

people to choose their own books. They also generally stock books with large type and talking books (audio tapes) for people with sight problems.

People from ethnic minority communities may be particularly isolated, and effort should be made to put them in contact with the appropriate community groups.

Personal family carers should be put in touch with the local carers support group, if they have not already contacted them.

Can you think of other ways of stimulating a person's interest in life and involving them in activities? What do you think you would do if you found yourself in this position? How would you react? What would you do to fill your time?

CHANGES IN HEALTH

We have emphasised that you as the Home Care Assistant will frequently be the person who is in the most regular contact with the person you are caring for, and therefore best placed to notice any changes in their physical or mental health which may require medical help or intervention or a reassessment of their care needs.

You therefore need to develop the skill of (unobtrusive) observation, to note any physical or mental changes over time, which might indicate a deterioration in health. Typical signs include the following:

clumsiness of fingers	confusion
deterioration of hearing or sight	dizziness
loss of appetite	loss of mobility
memory loss	mood changes
shakiness	

Any such symptoms should always be noted and, with the person's (or their carer's) consent, reported to the doctor or district nurse. It may be the policy of your employer that you should inform your line manager – check what the policy and procedure are.

Signs of ill health that could give immediate cause for alarm will be found in Chapter 6.

Medical matters should always be discussed in private, but ask people how they feel and encourage them to talk about their symptoms. If necessary or appropriate, discuss with them whether they need to see a doctor. If you have the slightest cause for concern, this should be reported to your line manager.

Encourage annual dental checks, testing of eyesight every two years and hearing checks whenever necessary. Make sure that items such as hearing aids and dentures are regularly cleaned. Arrangements can often be made for dentists, opticians and hearing therapists to visit people in their own home. Your local community health unit (or trust) should be able to advise you on this.

Diet is important in maintaining health and this is covered in the next chapter – 'Eating and Nutrition'.

STANDARD HYGIENE PROCEDURES

Always observe standard hygiene procedures to protect you and the person you are caring for against the spread of infection. General measures include:

- Always keep any cuts or grazes covered while they are healing. Use a waterproof adhesive dressing and replace frequently.
- Wash hands thoroughly:
  before and after contact with food;
  before and after carrying out first-aid procedures involving external bleeding and/or broken skin;
  after contact with blood or body fluids (urine, faeces, semen, vomit, sputum or tears).
- Use disposable gloves and an apron when carrying out first-aid procedures. The gloves should be seamless, well-fitting and intact.
- When mopping up spillages, handling heavily soiled materials or using bleach, always use household quality rubber gloves. It is a good idea to keep a different colour for different tasks, so that they can be readily identified.
- Never share items that may become contaminated with blood (eg towels, razor blades, toothbrushes). These should be for individual use only.

THE EFFECTS OF COLD AND LOW TEMPERATURES

The average winter temperature indoors is 18–24 °Celsius (64–75 °Fahrenheit). If the temperature falls below 16 °C (61 °F), people have reduced resistance to respiratory infections. Below 12 °C (54 °F) there is an increase in blood pressure and in the viscosity ('stickiness' and 'thickness') of blood, and below 9 °C (48 °F) the deep body temperature falls after two or more hours. It has been estimated that for every degree Celcius the winter is colder than average there are 8,000 'excess deaths' in the United Kingdom, the death rate increasing sharply from the age of 65.

As a result of low temperatures, older people are particularly at risk from respiratory problems, stroke, heart attack and hypothermia.

The body temperature becomes abnormally low because the body's controlling mechanisms do not work as effectively in old, or very young, people. Hypothermia, if not treated, can lead to unconsciousness and death.

Contributing factors include:

- immobility (for whatever reason);
- low income – causing fear of using heating systems to their full effect because of the cost;
- a tendency to fall, particularly if unable to get up from the floor;
- alcohol abuse;
- some mental illnesses and the medicines used to treat them;
- living alone, with no visitors.

Symptoms of hypothermia include:

- coldness and puffy face and skin, cold to the touch;
- coldness of unexposed skin (eg armpit);
- drowsiness;
- mental confusion;
- slurred speech;
- unsteady movement.

You should be aware of the danger of hypothermia and advise the people you are caring for on how to avoid the risk. You can obtain leaflets from your local GP.

If you arrive at a person's home and you suspect that they may be suffering from hypothermia:

1   Immediately contact their GP.

2   Wrap the person in blankets.

3   Turn the heating on or up.

4   If blankets or warm clothing are not available, aluminium foil or newspapers are effective in preventing further heat loss.

Do not move the person from their position.

Do not attempt to apply direct heat to the skin by rubbing or use of a hot water bottle.

ASSISTING WITH MEDICATION

It is often very difficult to find someone to help an older person with their medicines. There may be no relatives nearby, and community nurses are increasingly busy; as Home Care Assistant, you may be asked to help. If you have no training, there is a small risk that you could make a mistake with medicines and harm the person. There is a larger risk that any deterioration in the person's condition could be wrongly said to be due to your action. Employers usually take out insurance to cover their employees against these risks. Always check first with your line manager before being involved with assisting in giving medication.

Your managers should give you clear guidelines as to whether and in what ways you may help someone with their medicines. Ask about this if you are unsure what to do.

If helping with medicines is part of your job, it will usually be medicines taken by mouth or by inhalation that will concern you. Injected drugs or suppositories should be given *only* by trained staff such as nurses, or occasionally by properly instructed family members. You should always follow the instructions printed on the bottle or box. Ask advice from the doctor or pharmacist if you do not know what to do. Never alter the treatment plan on your own account without taking advice; for instance, you should *not* give a double dose of a medicine if one dose has been missed.

If your job description forbids you to help with medicines, you should not do so. If you are asked to give this sort of help, you should refuse politely and firmly, and refer the person who has asked you to your line manager for further discussion. In some cases you may find it difficult to follow policy instructions, perhaps because circumstances have changed since decisions were made. If this is so, you should arrange to discuss the situation with your line manager, so that you can explain your difficulties and new guidelines can be laid down if appropriate.

CARING FOR PEOPLE WHO ARE CONFUSED

Confusion may have many causes, but is never due to ageing alone. Treatment may help and even cure the problem. Try to make sure that a cause is sought so that suitable help can be arranged.

Many older people living at home exhibit some degree of confusion. Memory loss, combined with disorientation and wandering, can be very difficult and tiring to deal with. Nevertheless the aim of any support provided should be to improve the person's quality of life and to seek ways of eliminating or reducing the confusion, if this is possible.

You will require patience and understanding. Many people who are confused live with personal family carers who will need help as well. If they have been caring alone for a confused person for any length of time, they are likely to be both physically and mentally exhausted.

There are many different possible physical causes of confusion in older people. It should therefore always be assumed that some improvement could be possible.

- With the agreement of the older person, and their family carer, or your line manager if necessary, arrange a medical examination if confusion occurs or increases.
- Try to make sense of irrational behaviour.

- Do not label as 'confused' people who may just be forgetful, temporarily disorientated or having difficulty hearing.

Try to understand confused behaviour or speech. Find out about:

- previous medical history, personality and mental state;
- previous social skills and habits, including social isolation, or loss of independence;
- current medication;
- recent major events such as admission to hospital or a bereavement;
- possible sight or hearing impairment;
- any recurring patterns of abnormal behaviour.

Correct mistakes gently, without direct contradiction. Distract on to safer topics if necessary; getting the confused person to think of something else may change behaviour that is putting others at risk or causing distress.

The purpose and value of trying to contradict confused ideas have to be understood so that you as the Home Care Assistant know why you are correcting them.

'Reality orientation' is the name given to the technique of communicating with a confused person and trying to keep them in touch with reality. Try using these approaches:

- Give frequent reminders of time, place and identity.
- Use the person's name frequently.
- Gently, but firmly, correct confused behaviour, but avoid confrontation.
- Reinforce non-confused behaviour with praise.

To help confused people keep in touch with reality, the following may be of assistance:

- Large clocks or calendars, provided they are kept up to date.
- Well placed mirrors.

You may also need sensitivity in dealing with neighbours and other family carers, who may have different views on what constitutes appropriate care for the confused person. They may not understand the **rights** the person has to remain in their own home with all the risks that this entails.

PEOPLE WHO ARE AGGRESSIVE

When caring for people who may become aggressive, there could be a risk of physical attack. Training should be available to all Home Care Assistants to increase their understanding of the causes of aggression and the way in which potentially violent situations should be handled: you could ask about this.

It may not be the person you are caring for who is aggressive, but a member of the family.

You should never go alone in situations where aggression is thought to be likely. Two Home Care Assistants should be present (with one perhaps discreetly in the background). Any attack must be reported to your line manager immediately. If the attack leads to injury – however minor – you must follow the normal accident-reporting procedure.

PEOPLE WHO REFUSE TO CARE FOR THEMSELVES

It is not uncommon for Home Care Assistants to be faced with the problem of a person who appears to be acting against their own best interests by putting themselves (and maybe others) at risk in some way. They may, for example, refuse to take a bath or even wash; live in a dirty and infested house; fill their home with old newspapers; keep many cats – all these situations can happen.

There can be no specific guidelines for coping with these situations, as each set of circumstances will be different.

All such occurrences should be reported to your line manager in order to discuss ways of overcoming the difficulty. Provided there is no unacceptable risk to health or safety, or serious interference with the rights of other people, the situation may have to be accepted. Whatever the outcome, it is important to understand and to remain sympathetic to the needs and wishes of each individual person.

Please see also 'Working in Dirty Homes' in Chapter 6.

Always remember that the prime responsibility for the mental and physical health of the person rests with the GP, district nurse, community psychiatric nurse or other involved health professional. The role of the Home Care Assistant is to play a part in promoting the health care of the person under medical guidance and, in difficult cases, under medical supervision. A Home Care Assistant is not a nurse, and must not try to act like one.

One final point is worth making. You are not expected to like everyone simply because they have become old and in need of care. It is not human nature to like and get on with everyone you meet. Although, as mentioned in Chapter 2, many agencies will make every effort to match the personalities of the person needing care and their Home Care Assistant, you may, on occasions, still find yourself providing care to someone you do not really like. That is a natural human reaction. Remember that someone who was difficult to please and bad tempered when young is almost certain to be just the same when they are old!

CASE STUDY 1

Mrs W, aged 78, was referred to the social services department because of 'self-neglect'. She was badly nourished, apathetic and sometimes confused; she had got to the point where she apparently couldn't be bothered to feed herself.

She was seen by a social worker and home care manager, and it was decided that she should be provided with home care, seven days a week. She was also referred to the health service, who arranged for her to be visited regularly by a district nurse and a chiropodist.

The main tasks of the Home Care Assistants were to provide her with meals, to help her to cope with housework and to try to stimulate her and rekindle her interest. Within a fortnight, Mrs W was much improved and began, with encouragement, to participate in her own care. The home care service was gradually reduced to the level of two visits each week. 'Meals on wheels' were provided on the other days of the week and arrangements were made for Mrs W to attend a day centre twice a week, where she was able to join others in a range of activities providing social stimulation.

As a result of this programme of care, Mrs W became much improved and better able to care for herself. She began to take an interest in life, and her physical and mental health were greatly improved. The home care service was reduced to 'maintenance level', chiefly to keep Mrs W's condition under review.

Questions

1 *What individual skills did Home Care Assistants use in caring for Mrs W?*

2 *Wouldn't it have been less risky to have admitted Mrs W to an older persons' home, at least for a few weeks, until she improved?*

3 *What should be the main consideration in deciding on the package of care for Mrs W?*

CASE STUDY 2

Mr B is 80 years old. For the past five years he has lived in a one-bedroom flat with his divorced daughter, Mrs G. Mrs G sleeps on a camp bed in the living room. Until now she has not requested any form of help with her father.

Over the past few months Mr B's behaviour has become problematic. He has taken to walking around the flat at night shouting, and turning on taps in the bathroom. He is often confused and appears to be suffering from loss of memory. The neighbours have complained to Mrs G and to the landlord of the block in which they live.

Mrs G has found it increasingly difficult to cope with her part-time job, the demands of her father and the pressure from the neighbours. She has told one neighbour that she wishes her father would just 'get on and die', although on other occasions she says 'he's my dad, he's all I've got'.

Mrs G has begun to lose weight and has become short tempered with her father and at times has hit him. When she goes out to work she locks him in the bedroom to prevent him damaging anything. After a particularly violent confrontation with her father, Mrs G locked him in the bedroom and went to the local SSD offices where she demanded that they 'do something'.

Mr B has no wish to be admitted to a home for older people and Mrs G might be prepared to continue to care for him under different circumstances.

Questions

1   *What help do you think Mrs G requires?*

2   *Is there any difference between the needs of Mr B and those of Mrs G?*

3   *How do you think you would respond to Mr B and to Mrs G?*

KEY POINTS

- Ageing is a perfectly natural process but people age at different rates and show different signs of ageing.

- The mental and physical condition of an older person can often improve.

- People should never be described as illnesses (eg 'diabetics'). The emphasis must always be on the person, not their illnesses or disabilities.

- Caring for the person's emotional, psychological and social well-being is as important as meeting their physical needs.

- The Home Care Assistant is the most likely person to notice changes in the physical or mental health of the person they are caring for. These should be reported immediately.

- Always observe standard hygiene procedures to protect both you and the person you are caring for from the risk of infection.

- Watch out for signs of hypothermia and know what action to take.

- Assist with the administration of medication only with the full knowledge of the person's GP, district nurse and your line manager.

- You will require endless patience and understanding when caring for people who are confused. Reality orientation – trying to keep them in touch with reality – may assist.

- Never visit on your own any home where there is the potential danger of an aggressive or violent attack. Make sure you are accompanied.

- It is perfectly normal for you not to like all the people you care for. After all, not everyone is nice!

- The prime responsibility for the mental and physical well-being of the person rests with their GP and district nurse.

5 Eating and Nutrition

This chapter looks at the importance of food to people needing care, and identifies the main components of a healthy diet. It examines some aspects of preparing meals and the range of alternative means of providing nutritious food to people who are unable to cook it for themselves. Finally, this chapter provides some guidance on helping people to eat and drink.

Eating food is an important part of everyone's routine but meals are particularly significant for people who are housebound. Meal times should be looked forward to, and you should spend time with people while they eat.

You as the Home Care Assistant have an important role in promoting nutrition, the health and the general well-being of the people you are caring for. You will be helping them with choosing, buying and preparing food, and, if necessary, helping them to eat.

As with all other home care activities, people being cared for should be able to choose for themselves what they wish to eat. As far as possible, they should be encouraged to prepare and cook as much of the meal as they are able themselves. Many, however, will need help.

Some people lose their appetites when they get older and may need to be tempted to eat with appetising tasty food that they particularly like. Others may retain their appetites into very old age and have a special liking for the foods they were brought up on as children, such as stews, puddings, pies and offal.

THE IMPORTANCE OF A HEALTHY DIET

There is a saying that 'we are what we eat'. It is the food we eat and drink that keeps us healthy (nourishes us) and gives us energy. Too little food – or for that matter too much – can cause health problems and make us vulnerable to illness and disease.

It is advisable (although not essential) to eat a hot cooked meal every day to stay healthy, particularly in winter. A well balanced diet should contain a balance of the following foods:

- roughage – eg bran, wholemeal bread, fruit and vegetables (to prevent constipation);
- pasta or rice;
- lean red meat and poultry;
- oily fish such as sardines, mackerel and tuna;
- plenty of fluids.

Foods to avoid or have in moderation include:

- any food with high sugar content (sweets, cakes, pastry);
- saturated fat – found in butter, some cooking oils, some cheese, full cream milk;
- any fried food (grilled is better).

Older people, particularly those who are housebound, can be deficient in vitamin D, which is essential to keep bones healthy. This vitamin is absorbed from oily fish and breakfast cereals and from exposure to sunlight.

Think about the food you eat. Do you think that, in general, you follow a healthy diet? Could it be improved? How do you think you could best advise the people you are caring for about their diet?

If you want to find out more about healthy diets, your GP practice will be able to recommend suitable booklets or leaflets.

There may be some constraints on what the person you are caring for can eat, as a result of illness or disability. As a general principle, though, everyone should be able to eat and drink whatever they choose.

As the Home Care Assistant you should know, from the start, if anyone you are caring for has any particular dietary requirements. This should be part of the care plan. You should also always discuss with each individual person their personal likes, preferences and dislikes with regard to food and drink.

In time you will get to know and remember each person's likes and dislikes. But it may help to write them down first of all so that you don't forget.

You may find that some people who are housebound have little or no interest in eating and food because they are depressed or unhappy. It is essential to encourage them to eat by turning the meal into a social occasion and tempting the appetite with the suggestion of particular foods.

Remember the old saying, 'a little of what you fancy does you good'. The occasional 'treat' can help sustain the older person's interest in what they are eating.

The person you are caring for may, for medical purposes, follow a particular diet devised or recommended by their GP or a dietitian. You can help by supervising the diet and encouraging the person to eat only the foods that form part of the diet.

However, no one should ever be forced or coerced into eating what they do not want. If there are difficulties, discuss them first with the person concerned. If they continue to request or eat food that is not recommended in the diet, you may need to inform the GP, nurse or dietitian. But you should take this course of action only through your line manager, and you should always tell the person you are caring for what you are going to do.

Some religions have particular dietary laws and requirements that specify certain types of food – for example, Kosher and Halal. Every effort should be made to provide meals that are cooked according to the religious laws. Seek advice if necessary.

Some people you are caring for may be vegetarians or vegans (people who do not eat *any* animal products). Their food preferences must be respected and they should be assisted in having the food they specify. Seek help from your employing organisation if necessary. You should also be aware of possible problems if you yourself are vegetarian or vegan and are required to cook, or to help someone eat, a meal that includes meat or animal products.

How do you feel about this? Would you be able to prepare the food? Remember that the person you are caring for has the same **right** to choose to eat meat that you have to choose not to.

BUYING AND STORING FOOD

Allow the person you are caring for to choose what they want to eat and what you should buy. If necessary, give advice on budgeting and on the relative cost of foods. You should encourage each person to have as varied a diet as possible, within the limits of their budget.

You may need to purchase some foods that the people can prepare easily for themselves when you are not there. Remember that opening tinned food needs skill, dexterity and motivation, and this is therefore less likely to be eaten by people who do not have these abilities. An occupational therapist can advise on special tin openers that are available for people who have difficulty using standard tin openers.

Ensure that all food is stored correctly, and always in accordance with the instructions on the packaging. A person with poor vision may need help in labelling food, using either large print or braille.

If frozen food is purchased (or provided by Meals on Wheels), make certain that it can be stored at the correct temperature.

PREPARING FOOD

Always use care when handling food. Remember to wash your hands before touching food and to always use clean containers and utensils.

Involve the person as much as possible in helping you prepare the food.

When preparing food, make sure it's what the person wishes to eat and cook it according to the way they want it. Present it in an attractive way and try to 'balance' it with the other meals that are likely to be taken that day.

If your hours allow it, you should, on occasions, be present in the home when the person is eating a meal. You will provide company and stimulation, helping them to enjoy the meal all the more. It will also provide an opportunity to note discreetly exactly how much they do eat, and if they are experiencing any difficulty. For example, any difficulty in feeding themselves may indicate the onset of loss of manual dexterity or muscular control, and problems with chewing the food may indicate a need for a new set of dentures!

When caring for a visually impaired person, it is important to find out if they are receiving help from a rehabilitation worker in the social services department, whose job it is to teach people daily living skills within the home. If rehabilitation is being offered, you should liaise with the rehabilitation worker and see if you can assist in the programme.

If the person is not receiving help, you should find out which activities in the kitchen they feel competent to undertake and which they need help with. People with the same eye condition will vary over whether they feel confident enough to use hot saucepans, cut up vegetables or pour hot liquids. If you think the person could learn to do more themselves, you should, with their permission, seek the assistance of a rehabilitation worker.

ALTERNATIVE SOURCES OF FOOD

When the person with care needs has difficulty in preparing food, meals might be provided by the Meals on Wheels service, day centres and luncheon clubs, family, friends and neighbours, as well as the Home Care Assistant.

'Meals on wheels' may be delivered in a number of ways. The meal may be delivered already plated and 'hot', ready to eat. It may be a 'cook/chill' meal, heated up at a time to suit the service user, or it may take the form of frozen meals kept in a freezer until required.

If frozen meals are provided, make sure that the oven can be used without undue risk and that the food can be heated safely according to the instructions provided. Always check the 'use by' date on the meal to ensure that it is still safe to eat.

The problem with most of the 'meals on wheels' is that, although they can ensure the person has a hot and nutritious meal at regular intervals, they are rarely sufficiently flexible to take into account individual food preferences.

Sometimes your role as the Home Care Assistant will be to supplement these sources by, for example, preparing a breakfast or supper. Where possible, and sometimes with your help, the person may be able to visit a restaurant or go for a pub lunch or have a 'take away'. It is important to try to provide 'treats' of a special meal or type of food whenever possible.

The introduction of community care and the development of flexible care packages are likely to lead to a wide range of new, flexible ways of providing meals to people in their own homes. For example, the local pub or private residential home may be contracted to deliver meals to local people.

ALCOHOL

Many people enjoy drinking alcohol and this will apply to very many of the people you will be caring for.

For some, an alcoholic drink is seen either as a good appetite stimulant or as an enjoyable night-cap. If taken in excess, alcohol may cause diarrhoea, and increase the risk of falling.

There is a view that a very small intake of alcohol can be beneficial. Current health advice indicates that men should drink no more than 21 'units' of alcohol a week, and women 14. A unit is equal to half a pint of ordinary beer, or a pub measure of wine or spirits. These are the *upper* limits that are recommended.

You should remember that certain medication, especially sedatives or tranquillisers, may not mix with alcohol, and could cause drowsiness or, alternatively, increasing restlessness at night. You may need to remind the person you are caring for of this.

If you are concerned about the possibility of alcohol abuse (and that is not an easily defined term), it should be discussed first with your line manager before deciding on the appropriate action. It might then be mentioned to the person's GP or district nurse.

However, as a Home Care Assistant you should always take care not to apply or impose your own personal standards and beliefs on the people you are caring for.

Remember that it is always a fine balance between respecting the independence, choice, right to privacy and confidentiality of the people you are caring for and the need to refer to others such as their GP when you consider that they may be putting their health at risk.

ASSISTANCE WITH EATING

Some people needing care may require varying degrees of assistance with eating. The Home Care Assistant should provide this help with tact and good humour. **Remember** at all times to help in such a way that it preserves the dignity of the individual person.

Where possible, meals should be provided at a time that suits each individual person, encouraging their participation in the choice of menu. The food should always be laid out so that it looks attractive and appetising to eat.

Think about what you like. What makes you want to eat a meal?

Where appetite is small as a result of little physical activity, or loss of sight, taste or smell, it is particularly important to tempt with at least a sample portion of the meal.

It is important to maximise independence for people with disabilities by ensuring that appropriate eating aids are available. Where necessary, seek the help and advice of an occupational therapist or a rehabilitation worker. Care and discretion should be exercised when introducing new utensils, seeking the person's willingness to cooperate.

Patience and understanding are needed when helping frail people with their food. Judge whether to help with advice and encouragement, or if you need to give greater assistance. Always ask the person before cutting up food on the plate, guiding the hands or providing full assistance.

Cut up food in accordance with the wishes of the person you are assisting. If giving full assistance, always give the person exactly what they ask for. Allow plenty of time, and ensure that the person is able to indicate what they like, what they do not like and how much they want. Make sure that the food is at a suitable temperature, neither too cold nor too hot, and that you do not place the person in danger of choking by offering too large mouthfuls.

Put yourself in the place of the person you are assisting. How do you think you would feel, not being able to feed yourself? How would you want the person helping you to respond? What would you want them to do for you?

ASSISTING CONFUSED PEOPLE

Confused older people may forget to eat and will need persuasion and encouragement to ensure that they eat regularly. People who are suffering from dementia are particularly at risk of an inadequate diet and nutrition: meals may be taken irregularly or forgotten altogether, as the sufferers have difficulty in distinguishing the time of day.

Dementia sufferers may lose weight and eat less as the illness progresses. Chewing and swallowing processes often slow down because of the difficulty in coordinating the muscles that control swallowing. Someone with a neurological condition, such as Parkinson's disease, may also have difficulty with chewing and swallowing. Allow extra time for this.

If a person totally refuses to eat, the doctor must be consulted. Encouragement should be given to take as much fluid as possible.

Remember to try to encourage people to feed themselves as much as possible.

Remember to allow plenty of time and avoid rushing.

CASE STUDY 1

Mr B was a 76-year-old widower, living on his own in a small terraced house. His furnishings were very basic; there was a general feeling of neglect about both the house and Mr B. He was a heavy drinker, and most of his income was spent on alcohol. He didn't bother very much about feeding himself and so was undernourished. He was a cheery outgoing type of man and was known in the locality as a bit of a character.

One day the police were called when neighbours reported that Mr B had not been seen for over two days. They broke in to find him collapsed; he was admitted to hospital for a check-up and observation. After a week, he was discharged home; in the meantime social services were alerted. After assessment he was allocated a Home Care Assistant for four visits a week.

The Home Care Assistant persuaded Mr B to improve his diet and helped him to buy and prepare food. She was able, through her agency, to get some furniture and clothes. She also worked to improve the appearance and cleanliness of the house.

She talked to Mr B about his drinking, as did a social worker. He didn't consider that he had a problem. He didn't need help. He did not want to be put in touch with Alcoholics Anonymous. He wanted to go on drinking as before. His decision was respected. When he had sufficiently improved, his Home Care Assistant's visits to him were reduced to a 'watching' level of once a week.

Questions

1 *What individual skills do you think the Home Care Assistant used in caring for Mr B?*

2 *What other services might have been provided for him   in the short term and in the long term?*

3 *Should more have been done to deal with his drinking? If so, what?*

4 *Could he have been dealt with differently following his collapse? If so, how?*

CASE STUDY 2

Mr M, 81 years old, had been recently widowed. Over the past six years his eyesight had been deteriorating. Although he had some useful sight for getting around, his central vision was poor and it was hard for him to focus on objects. Home care had been arranged for him on the death of his wife, to help him with housework and with shopping and preparing meals.

The Home Care Assistant learned from Mr M that he was receiving help from a rehabilitation worker. With his permission, she got in touch and learnt that the rehabilitation worker had been teaching Mr M to pour hot liquids safely. The Home Care Assistant then suggested that Mr M should make coffee for them both in the mornings while she was working upstairs. She realised that Mr M might feel embarrassed if she was watching him. She knew that it would take longer for Mr M to prepare the coffee and that there might be more mess than if she did it herself, but the dignity he would gain and the confidence of feeling useful would outweigh other considerations.

Questions

1 *What else could the Home Care Assistant suggest that Mr M should do?*

2 *How could you assist the rehabilitation worker further with Mr M?*

KEY POINTS

- The Home Care Assistant should ensure that the people eat a nutritious meal at least once a day, have a varied diet and try to keep to any medical diet they may be on.

- The people concerned should choose for themselves what they wish to eat, and, as far as possible, should be involved in its preparation.

- Tempt people to eat by making the meal time a social occasion, presenting the food attractively and from time to time providing food that you know they particularly like.

- Make sure you are aware of the dietary laws and requirements of certain religions. Also of anyone who is vegetarian or vegan.

- Always take great care when handling food. Remember to wash your hands before touching the food and to use clean utensils and containers.

- Alcohol should not be drunk if the person is on medication such as tranquillisers and sedatives.

- Assist people with their food only if they really do need assistance and if they agree to you helping. Special utensils and other aids may help people with disabilities to help themselves and retain their independence.

6 Health and Safety, including Accidents and Emergencies

This chapter looks at aspects of health and safety and the need to adopt safe working practices. It considers the most common accidents and emergencies that occur and gives some outline guidance. Security in the home is also covered. Finally, there is a discussion of the implications of working in dirty and infested homes.

HEALTH AND SAFETY

All employing organisations have to comply with the requirements of the Health and Safety at Work etc Act 1974. However, there are some features in relation to the provision of care to people in their own home that are beyond the scope of the Act. Also, in the case of privately provided home care, it may be the responsibility of the person receiving care to provide a safe working environment.

As a Home Care Assistant you must have concern for your own health and safety as well as for those who receive your help and support, their personal family carers and their visitors

Just as in one's own home or any busy workplace, this means using commonsense, taking normal precautions and thinking ahead.

All organisations employing Home Care Assistants should have a written health and safety policy specifically related to the provision of home care services. A copy of this should be given to all employees at the start of their employment. The policy should be regularly reviewed and updated.

Ensure that you are familiar with the health and safety policy and regulations of your department or agency. For example, there may be specific regulations concerning the use of ladders.

If you are employed directly by a local authority social services department (SSD) or a private or voluntary organisation, you are covered by the Health and Safety at Work Act. If you are registered as self-employed and paid by the person you are caring for, you are not covered by the Act. You may need to ensure that both you and the person you are caring for have adequate insurance cover in case of accidents being caused to one or other of you as the result of a mistake or negligence.

The nature of home care means that you will be working in a variety of places that are not 'workplaces' in the usual sense of the word. Homes can be very dangerous places. More accidents occur in the home than elsewhere. The Royal Society for the Prevention of Accidents (RoSPA) estimated that, in 1990, there were 3.1 million accidents in the home which resulted in a recorded visit to a hospital or GP.

If you are employed by a local authority SSD, an inspection of the home will have been carried out, and any potential hazards formally noted, before the first visit of the Home Care Assistant. You must be aware of the potential dangers in each home and should always be vigilant about safety matters, for the sake of the person living in the home as well as for yourself. Potential hazards should always be pointed out and, if possible, discussed with the home owner in the first instance. If the person is unable or unwilling to correct the hazard, it should immediately be reported to your line manager for appropriate action to put it right.

You must never use unsafe equipment. The person you are caring for has a responsibility to minimise any hazard, but cannot be required to correct it. There can therefore at times be conflict between the need to provide care services to a vulnerable person and the need to safeguard the health and safety of an employee.

The last resort is the withdrawal of care services. Naturally, agencies are extremely reluctant to do this and it only ever happens following a full discussion with the person concerned and exploration of all possible alternatives.

HAZARDS OF LIFTING AND HANDLING

Thirty per cent of injuries are caused by manual lifting and handling activities. A new European Directive on manual lifting and handling came into effect in January 1993. The current legal position is that nobody should lift, move or carry a load so heavy that it is likely to cause injury.

This legislation affects your work as a Home Care Assistant. You should receive training in lifting and handling techniques as part of your induction, but in any case you should never attempt to lift heavy loads on your own.

With the proper training, you can assist the people you are caring for and help them get in and out of a chair, bed or bath. However, you should never actually lift them yourself, even if there are two of you to do this. If lifting is required, hoists should be installed for the purpose.

Whenever lifting any object or helping the person you are caring for, you should be aware that serious injury can be caused to either or both of you if the correct procedure is not followed. In an emergency, seek help.

CHECKLIST – HAZARDS IN THE HOME

Watch out in particular for:

- Faulty electrical equipment, particularly the following:
  badly wired plugs;
  overloaded sockets;
  frayed cable;
  wrong fuse rating;
  dangerous, free-standing electric fires;
  long trailing electrical cables.

  NOTE Never take electrical equipment home with you to repair. You may be personally liable if something then goes wrong and an accident occurs.

- Faulty gas appliances (gas companies will often provide free checks for older customers).
  Be careful also of appliances using bottled gas.
  Gas taps accidentally left on.

- Mats and rugs on polished floors.
  Worn and damaged carpets.
  Dangerous and loose stair treads.
  Wet and slippery floors.
  Furniture placed in awkward positions.
- Faulty stepladders.
  Using chairs and tables in place of ladders.
- Faulty cooking utensils – eg loose handles, worn pans.
  Chipped glassware or china.
- Inadequate lighting – making it difficult to see potential hazards.
- Clothes draped over heaters to dry.

Can you add any other items to this list?

ACCIDENTS AND EMERGENCIES

Hopefully you will very rarely find yourself in the situation of dealing with accidents or emergencies, but it is essential that you know the correct course of action to take, if and when you do.

Accidents and emergencies come in all shapes and sizes. Some are more life threatening, and therefore urgent, than others. In general you are most likely to discover the accident or emergency on arrival at the person's home. The most common form of emergency is a medical emergency which may or may not have been caused by some form of physical accident. Fire, flood and burglary are other emergencies that you may encounter.

As we have already seen, very often the Home Care Assistant will be the only person to see the person needing care on a regular, sometimes daily, basis. In Chapter 3 it is emphasised that the Home Care Assistant is often the one who is most likely to notice changes in appearance or behaviour that could indicate that the person may need help. It is not an exaggeration to say that the Home Care Assistant can often be the 'eyes and ears' of the care agency and of health and social services departments, and can provide early warning of any problems that the person may be experiencing.

In many situations, such as an accident or burglary, it is not unknown for the person to wait for the Home Care Assistant to arrive – someone who is familiar and trusted – before telling anyone about it.

Ideally, you should have received basic first-aid training as part of your induction training. However, realistically, this is much more likely to happen after you have been working for some length of time.

When first introduced to the person needing care (see Chapter 2), you should be informed of any pre-existing medical conditions. This should help you as the Home Care Assistant to understand and possibly anticipate what might happen to the person you are caring for. For example, if they suffer from diabetes (however mild) and they are found unconscious, it **may** be because of the diabetes. It may, however, be something else entirely, so you must always keep an open mind.

Without being intrusive and over-fussy, you should look out for the following signs when visiting each person:

- Any unexpected changes in behaviour or mood.
- Complaints of pain, giddiness or breathing difficulties.
- Untypical confusion or forgetfulness.
- Any degree of paralysis or loss of control of limbs.
- Signs of injury which may have been caused by a fall.
- Signs of non-accidental injury which might have been caused by a physical assault.
- Signs of drug or alcohol overdose.
- Burns or scalds.

The following is a checklist of the appropriate action to take if you arrive at someone's home and find them in a collapsed state or very ill.

CHECKLIST – WHAT TO DO IN A MEDICAL EMERGENCY

- Try to stay calm, and take a few moments to plan your best course of action.
- Check that the person's airway is clear. Turn them into the recovery position if necessary.
- Never assume that the person is dead.

- Control bleeding by pressing on the bleeding point through a pad of whatever clean material is available (a towel or clean cloth, for example).

- If the person is conscious, try to get them to tell you what has happened, where it hurts, etc.

- If you think the person needs urgent attention, dial 999 and call the ambulance service without delay. Otherwise, call the person's GP.

- Do not move the person, unless:
  to clear the airway (see above);
  they are in obvious potential danger (eg from fire or traffic).

- Make the person comfortable by placing a pillow under their head and covering them with a blanket. However, *do not* move the head of someone who may have injured the neck or spine.

- You could send any tablets the person is taking, and their hospital appointment card, with them to the hospital. Give these to the ambulance staff.

- Notify the GP, your line manager and any other appropriate person (eg relative or close friend), telling them of the action you have taken.

NOTE It is assumed that you have knowledge of basic first aid. If you do not, summon assistance as fast as possible and stay calm.

CHECKLIST – INFORMATION YOU NEED TO KNOW IN AN EMERGENCY

- Basic first aid. (This should form part of your training.)

- The telephone number of key people: GP, relatives, friends, neighbours. This list should be kept in a prominent place, such as the front door or on the mantelpiece in the main living room (see Chapter 2).

- Location of the nearest telephone if the person doesn't have one.

- The nearest source of help (eg neighbour, family, friend) – but don't waste time seeking this help if the situation demands a 999 call.

- In the case of fire, follow the advice of the fire service:
  get out, **stay out** and **call for help**.

  Do your best to help others get out of the property, but don't put yourself at any risk.

It is quite common now for smoke detector alarms to be fitted in homes, particularly in warden-controlled sheltered housing. These can be very sensitive and be set to go off very easily, for example by the smoke from burning toast. It would be sensible to check whether any of the homes you visit have these alarms so that you know in advance and can take any necessary action.

Slipping and falling are common accidents, particularly when helping someone to wash or bathe. To minimise the possibility of such accidents occurring, ensure that wet and dirty floors are washed and dried without delay and that suitable footwear is worn. Mats or rugs can be hazards and are easy to trip over. With the person's consent, these should be removed.

You can prevent or reduce risk of injury or infection by taking care and adopting strict standards of hygiene and cleanliness. This is particularly important when helping someone to use the toilet or when washing soiled clothing or bedding.

You should always note any points of concern and discuss these with your line manager as soon as possible. Avoid wearing jewellery, as this can cause injury.

Any accident you are involved in, whether or not it involves anyone else, must, under the requirement of the Health and Safety at Work etc Act 1974, be reported and entered into the accident report book kept by your employer. (If you are self-employed you do not need to do this, but it would be sensible for the person you are caring for to be told about the accident, if they are not already aware of it.)

These are points for general guidance. Your employing agency should have written instructions on what to do in an emergency, and telling you of this should be part of your initial training.

Can you think of any accident or emergency situation you have found yourself in in the past? What action did you take? Do you think it was the right action? If not, you should make sure you do know what to do next time.

SECURITY IN THE HOME

You will find that some people are obsessive about security in their home, while others take a very casual approach.

As the Home Care Assistant visiting the home, you have a responsibility to ensure that you in no way put its security at risk. If there is an agreement for you to hold a key or collect the key from a neighbour, this agreement should be in writing. Never, ever encourage someone to leave the key under the mat, on a long string inside the letter box or some other obvious place. This is an invitation to crime.

If you think they can afford it, encourage the home owner to have good door and window locks fitted. A peep-hole and safety chain fitted to the front door will enable them to find out the identity of callers without opening the door fully. If they are on a low income, they may be able to get assistance to improve the security of their home. The local housing department and/or crime prevention officer should be able to advise; local voluntary groups, such as Age Concern, may fit it for them.

You should also always advise the people you care for to ask for the identity card of anyone calling. Anyone – including you – on official business should have such a card.

On leaving the home, always check that the door is shut securely. If you are leaving at night, you should seek the person's permission to check that windows and all other doors to the outside are securely fastened.

If someone is obsessive about security, they are likely to have a number of bolts and bars on their windows. If you arrive at the home and get no reply, try calling the person through the letter box. They may just have decided not to let you in. If they have a telephone and there is a telephone box close by, try ringing them. If there is still no reply, contact your line manager. You may need to call the police and ambulance if you think it is an emergency. On the other hand, they may have gone to visit relatives and forgot to inform the home care service!

WORKING IN DIRTY HOMES

As a Home Care Assistant you will not usually be required to be part of a 'dirty homes squad' but you will sometimes work in a home that is not clean or that is in the process of being cleaned.

The question of what is clean or dirty is subjective because people have differing standards. Normally, you will be concerned to ensure that the person's home is kept reasonably clean and hygienic but this will be difficult to achieve if the person you are caring for has very poor standards.

Some very dirty homes, and people, can be caused by:

- Very poor standards of hygiene and cleanliness over a long period, resulting in a dirty, smelly house.

- An 'eccentric' person whose generally poor standards are made worse by the collection and storage of rubbish such as newspapers, cans or bottles which fill the house and make cleaning impossible.

- Keeping a large number of pets, usually cats and dogs, with no regard for their proper care and management.

An almost inevitable outcome of all these conditions is the infestation of the dwelling with vermin.

You should know that, in general, everyone has the **right** to remain in their own home, however insanitary or hazardous the conditions. There are only two exceptions:

- People who are defined under the Mental Health Act 1983 as mentally disordered and are subject to compulsory admission to hospital.

- Under Section 47 of the National Assistance Act 1948, community physicians have powers to compulsorily remove from home people who are not mentally disordered but when it is in their own interest or to prevent injury to others. This power is very rarely used.

Most local authorities employ special teams of workers to carry out the difficult and distasteful task of cleaning dirty premises. They are usually employed by the social services, environmental health or cleansing departments of the authority and they require special protective clothing and equipment. Some local authorities provide the services by contracting private firms.

You should:

- Report immediately if someone's standards worsen to the point where their home is becoming dirty.

- Seek assistance if there are signs of infestation by, for example, rats, mice, cockroaches, bedbugs, lice (animal or human).

- Wear protective clothing if you are required to work in a dirty home or with a very dirty person. (Your employing agency should provide this.)

- Seek help, advice and training on domestic hygiene and on human infestation (eg head and body lice, scabies). You should be aware that you could become infested yourself and take appropriate precautionary measures. Your employer and your local pharmacist will advise you.

- Be aware of the health and safety factors involved in working in dirty homes.

Finally, despite the very real difficulties in working in such homes, try to maintain a sensitive approach.

CASE STUDY

Mr and Mrs C, a couple in their 80s, lived in a multi-storey block of flats. They were both fairly frail but coped quite well in the flat with the assistance of a Home Care Assistant who visited them three times a week to provide support and help with meals and shopping.

One morning the Home Care Assistant arrived at the Cs' flat to find that it had been flooded. An elderly neighbour in the flat above had gone away and left a tap running over a plugged sink. As a result, Mr and Mrs C's flat was drenched; the furniture and carpets were wet through; one of the ceilings had collapsed; and the electricity supply had failed. The flat was virtually uninhabitable, and Mr and Mrs C were cold, hungry and very distressed.

The Home Care Assistant's first action was to stop the source of the flooding. He then ensured that Mr and Mrs C were themselves dry and warm before reporting the matter to his supervisor. The supervisor together with a social worker and an area manager from the housing department arrived at the flat to assess the situation and identify what needed to be done.

Mr and Mr C, with their agreement, were taken to a residential home for older people for short-term care. The furniture and carpets were taken away by the direct labour department to be dried out. A check was made to see if the Cs had insurance for house contents. (They didn't.) The housing department started work on drying the flat, making good the damage and checking other nearby flats for damage.

After three weeks, Mr and Mrs C were able to return to their home.

Questions

1 *What individual skills do you think the Home Care Assistant used in caring for Mr and Mrs C?*

2 *Who else might have needed care?*

3 *Should any other person/agency have been involved at the beginning of this incident?*

4 *Did the couple* have *to go into a residential home?*

5 *Could choice have been exercised? If so, how?*

KEY POINTS

- Always observe the correct health and safety procedures.

- Never panic in an emergency. Assess the situation calmly before taking the appropriate action.

- Observe any changes in the condition of the person that could indicate the onset of any medical problem or emergency.

- Identify any major safety hazards in the home that could be a danger to you and/or the home owner. Try to persuade the home owner to get them put right.

- Advise the home owner on ways of making the home secure.

- Take great care when lifting. Back strain can be for life. Never attempt to lift a person yourself. Use a hoist

- Seek assistance if you think someone's home is becoming dirty and/or infested.

7 Mobility and Disability

Mobility means simply the action of getting from one place to another.

Keeping mobile and active is very important. Different people require differing degrees of help to remain mobile and their needs may vary over time. Mobility can easily decrease and dependence increase if people are left sitting around their homes for long periods.

You as the Home Care Assistant have a responsibility to try to maintain and support the people you are caring for and to ensure that they retain the maximum amount of independence possible in their lives. Mobility is a very important factor in maintaining independence.

PHYSICAL DIFFICULTIES EXPERIENCED BY OLDER PEOPLE

Older people frequently experience certain physical difficulties which may become disabilities and lead to a loss of mobility. These include difficulty with:

- Walking, which can lead to the need for walking aids and possibly, eventually, a wheelchair.
- Failing sight, causing lack of confidence in moving inside and outside the home.
- Using hands, especially for grasping, opening things, using switches, dressing, going to the toilet.
- Getting in or out of bed or the bath.

- Climbing stairs and negotiating furniture.
- Walking outside of the house, leading to a lack of confidence in crossing roads and busy junctions.

THE IMPORTANCE OF MOBILITY

The quality of life for some older people can worsen because they become housebound and isolated. This can happen over a long period, as the result of the death of a partner, or begin with a disabling illness or accident.

Older people, just like anyone else, can become depressed. However, it is easier for the cycle of depression to become self-reinforcing for older people. They can't be bothered to go out so they begin to lose their social skills and their mobility. The less they get out to shops, to see friends, to go to bingo or to church or the theatre, the less they become able to.

With appropriate professional advice you can help to halt this process and, if needed, with appropriate aids, can begin to restore mobility and confidence.

A positive approach to the provision of care can help to restore interest and purpose to the person's life. A balance must be struck between the real limitations of each individual and their actual potential abilities. This balance should be identified by all the people involved in decisions relating to the provision of care services – including the person needing care and any personal carers they may have, such as family and friends.

If care and help are being provided through a statutory body such as the local authority SSD or the health authority, each person being cared for should have a personal care plan. Decisions that are reached concerning the most effective means of maintaining the independence and mobility of the older person should be included in the care plan.

People with poor sight can be referred to a rehabilitation worker for an independent assessment.

Before starting to provide care, managers need to obtain detailed information about the capability of each person. This information must be shared and discussed with you, the person directly providing the care.

Only then will you have sufficient knowledge of the person's needs to give the appropriate level of care and support.

It is, however, a mistake to give too much help. It must be remembered that some instructions given as part of a care plan can seem harsh and uncaring, but they are vital to encourage independence. Dependency can be increased if help is always given to get out of a chair or to walk. In such cases, some individuals will quickly lose the will to move around independently.

Wherever possible, you should help and encourage each person to do as much as they can for themselves. This is not always easy. They may have already become dependent and it is not unknown for even relatively fit older people to expect to be 'looked after' in their later years. It is, however, better for their general state of health and personal confidence if you encourage them to help with bedmaking, dusting and food preparation than to always do these tasks for them.

CHECKLIST – EXAMPLES OF WAYS OF ENCOURAGING MOBILITY

- It is generally better to encourage a person to rise from a chair unassisted if they can.
- It may be more helpful to walk alongside a person without physically supporting them if they can manage.
- Allow people with visual loss to say how they wish to be guided.
- Wheelchairs must not be used merely to save time.
- Try to provide moral rather than physical support.
- Be aware when to be firm or gentle, or to negotiate.
- Show sympathy and praise effort. (Constant chivvying can be irritating and counter-productive.)
- Involve the person in undertaking tasks around the home; don't let them sit in a chair and watch you do it all.
- Put on some music and encourage them to move in time to it.
- Ensure that walking frames, when used, are always within reach, and are correctly adjusted to suit the height of the individual.
- An armchair suited to an individual's needs can make all the difference in enabling them to sit down and get up unaided.

- Wheelchairs* and other equipment should be regularly inspected and maintained.
- Be aware of safe practices when using walking aids or wheelchairs, and pass this information on to users, wherever possible.

THE IMPORTANCE OF EXERCISE

Exercise is important at any age, and most of us don't get enough of it. A certain amount of exercise, adapted to meet the particular needs of each person you are caring for, will improve strength, suppleness and stamina.

Try putting the radio or other music on and encouraging the person to move and 'dance' to the music. Keep-fit and music-and-movement exercises are good ways of encouraging mobility. You may find that these activities take place in a local day centre or residential home, and the person may be able to join in – although transport may have to be arranged.

Swimming is very good exercise at any age, but in particular for anyone who is overweight or has back problems or disabilities, as the water supports the body.

CARE OF FEET

Good foot care is essential for maintaining mobility and general functioning and therefore independence. Many problems with the feet can be prevented; whenever possible you should encourage the people you are caring for to wear properly fitting shoes that provide support, rather than slippers, as normal footwear.

You may need to wash a person's feet if they are unable to do so themselves. Take great care to dry between the toes as this can be a source of infection. **Never** cut toenails or attempt to treat corns. These must be

---

* If issued by the Disablement Services Authority, inspection should be carried out by the designated approved repairer. This information should have been given to the person at the time the wheelchair was issued.

done by a chiropodist because an accidental cut to the skin can cause infection, ulceration and even gangrene. People with diabetes or circulatory problems are particularly at risk. The chiropodist can also advise on the proper footwear.

EQUIPMENT THAT ASSISTS MOBILITY

Local authorities (usually through their social services departments) and health authorities can provide a range of equipment which will help people to cope with different kinds of disabilities. The equipment and adaptations that are generally available include:

- Walking aids such as sticks, pulpit (Zimmer) frames, crutches and wheelchairs. Assessment of need, help and advice on their use are available from physiotherapists, occupational therapists and/or aids assistants. As a general rule, the person should be encouraged to manage with the most simple aid that meets their needs, to avoid the danger of increasing dependency. For example, use one walking stick rather than two or use two walking sticks rather than a Zimmer.

- Symbol canes or long canes for people with poor sight who have received mobility training.

- A wide range of devices that help in reaching and grasping objects, in opening bottles and jars, in cooking and preparing food and drinks, and in dressing.

- Various types of lifts to enable people to go up and down stairs.

- General adaptations to the person's home to make it more easily accessible to them (eg ramps, downstairs toilet/bathroom, adapted kitchen).

- Aids and equipment to assist toileting and bathing, including hoists and sometimes the installation of a shower.

- Aids for people with poor vision. Also check on lighting and encourage the use of colour contrast (eg a red jug on a white surface is easier to see than a white jug on a white surface).

- Incontinence accessories and supplies (see also Chapter 8).

You need to know that such aids are available and where they can be obtained. Consult your line manager and/or occupational therapist if you think any special equipment may assist the person you are caring for.

The Disabled Living Foundation (address in Appendix 7) provides comprehensive information on all the equipment and aids that are available to assist people with daily living. The Royal National Institute for the Blind has information on aids for people with poor vision.

CARE OF PRESSURE AREAS

People who lack mobility – for whatever reason – and spend long periods sitting in chairs or lying in bed are prone to develop pressure sores. These occur where any bony point presses against an underlying surface. People who are very thin or obese, suffering from incontinence or poor circulation and are unable to move themselves easily are particularly likely to develop pressure sores.

You will need to understand the principles of care of pressure areas and the prevention of sores. However, Home Care Assistants should carry out care of pressure areas only under the supervision of a district or community nurse and only after having the appropriate training.

Prevention is helped by:

- A good diet.
- Ensuring absolute cleanliness of the skin (especially if the person is incontinent – see also Chapter 8).
- Moving the person's position every 2–3 hours to promote circulation.
- Keeping bedding and other covers smooth and free from crumbs.
- Avoiding friction in lifting.

If soreness occurs, the GP may prescribe cream for application to the infected area.

Pressure-relieving aids such as sheepskins, anti-pressure pads, urine-absorbing sheets and 'ripple pads' and mattresses can be helpful.

CASE STUDY 1

Mr and Mrs L had lived together for many years and were in their late 60s. Mr L had taken early retirement at the age of 52 to look after his wife who was becoming increasingly disabled owing to arthritis. As Mrs L's condition continued to worsen, she had severe walking difficulties, and her hands and knuckles had become swollen and very painful. Her husband 'did everything for her', and she had become dependent, losing all motivation to help herself. The couple had not sought, nor had they received, any assistance from social services. They had no close family, and Mr L had for years prided himself on his ability to care for his wife without outside help.

Mr L died of a heart attack at the age of 69. Suddenly, Mrs L was deprived of the love and support of a long-term carer; she had little ability or motivation to help herself. She was referred by neighbours to the GP and social services.

There was a swift assessment of Mrs L's needs and, with her agreement, she was admitted to hospital for an in-depth review of her condition, medication and level of functioning. Upon her discharge, there was an assessment by all agencies involved, in her own home, of her ability to cope. Various aids were provided, and Mrs L received occupational and physiotherapy support and treatment aimed at developing her independence. Throughout the whole process, Mrs L had been allocated a Home Care Assistant to provide help and support as she tried to establish herself in her own home. After a period of three months, Mrs L became able to care for herself with the services of a Home Care Assistant visiting three times a week and with some other domiciliary services.

Questions

1 *What individual skills do you think the Home Care Assistant used in caring for Mrs L?*

2 *Should somebody be aware of cases where a disabled older person is cared for by a single carer, so that problems may be anticipated?*

3 *If Mrs L had not improved sufficiently to be able to care for herself at least partially, what do you think would have been the outcome?*

NOTE It is not at all unusual for a disabled or chronically ill person to be cared for by an aged partner or relative. Nor is it unusual for the carer to die *before* the person receiving the care.

CASE STUDY 2

Miss L, 79 years old, lived by herself. She had severe sight problems due to glaucoma. Although she could focus well on objects directly in front of her, her side vision was very poor, and so going out alone was very frightening for her.

However, she very much wanted to get out to the corner shop by herself and her rehabilitation worker helped her, over a six-month period, build up the confidence to walk by herself to the shop.

Shortly afterwards a Home Care Assistant was asked to work with Miss L to help her with preparing meals and with housework. Soon the Home Care Assistant, out of kindness, started bringing Miss L a loaf of bread each day to save Miss L the bother of going out. Miss L thought it would be rude not to accept the help and quickly lost the confidence she had gained by going out by herself.

Questions

1   *What did the Home Care Assistant do wrong?*
2   *If you were Miss L's Home Care Assistant, how would you work with Miss L? What would you do?*

KEY POINTS

- Mobility is a key factor in maintaining independence.
- Involve the person in doing tasks around the home, in order to increase their mobility.
- Encourage the person to do simple keep-fit exercises.
- Make sure that care is taken of the feet and encourage the wearing of properly fitting shoes that provide support.
- Encourage the use of simple aids to assist mobility. Avoid the use of aids that are not necessary, as they will only increase dependence.

8 Maintaining Continence

To many people, the maintenance of continence is important to their self-respect and self-image. It is therefore very important to be able to help people to find ways to maintain continence, as this affects the rest of their well-being and general approach to life.

Incontinence should never be accepted as just 'part of getting old'.

Incontinence may occur at any age. It is not inevitable in old age but it does occur in both men and women and it can be a cause of great embarrassment and loss of self-esteem and self-confidence. Yet it can frequently be easily cured or at least improved by very simple measures. Whatever can be done to minimise its effect is always of great benefit to sufferers and their personal carers.

THE ONSET OF INCONTINENCE

Home Care Assistants may be the first to notice the onset of incontinence because of their regular contact with the people they are caring for.

Incontinence can be treated and in most cases, with proper management, the condition can be greatly improved or even cured. Maintaining continence should always be the main aim.

The sufferer may be incontinent of urine or faeces or both. Incontinence may be temporary – for example, due to infection or to emotional disturbances such as bereavement. It may, however, indicate the onset of deterioration of intellectual functioning (dementia).

Incontinence should always be referred to the GP, who may involve a specialist incontinence adviser – generally a district nurse.

Tact and discretion should be used to discuss the issue of incontinence with sufferers. They should be encouraged to seek medical help themselves, if at all possible.

People are very frequently ashamed of being incontinent. It is not unknown for people to go to considerable and sometimes bizarre lengths to hide the evidence of their incontinence, which may include hiding soiled clothing. This is often an indication that the person is aware that they are not managing to cope with this aspect of their life. Try to show understanding of the problem and acceptance of the reasons for it. This will encourage the sufferer to do something about it.

If the sufferer takes no action themselves, even with encouragement, and does not contact their GP or district nurse, you should report the situation to your line manager – but make certain that they know this is what you are going to do.

Even when it is not possible to make significant improvements in the condition, the tactful and sympathetic care that you and others provide can do a great deal to reduce the physical and emotional discomfort caused by the condition.

CAUSES OF INCONTINENCE

There is often no single cause of incontinence. It generally arises from a combination of both physical and environmental factors, most of which are not irreversible.

Physical factors include:

- urinary tract infections;
- diabetes;
- after-effects of a stroke;
- enlarged prostate gland (in men);
- some neurological conditions or infections can result in a loss of control;
- severe constipation;

- stress incontinence (a leakage of urine caused by a sneeze or a cough).

Drugs such as:

- sedatives and tranquillisers which diminish the sensation of needing to pass urine, and get to the lavatory in time;
- diuretics (water tablets), given to people for a number of conditions (including heart failure) to increase the ability of the body to rid itself of fluids;
- alcohol is also a diuretic, and drinking a large quantity of beer, etc, can cause a loss of control.

Psychological factors such as:

- anxiety;
- changes in life-style;
- worry over not being able to reach the lavatory in time and 'having an accident';
- loss of self-esteem and self-confidence;
- imagined or actual rejection by relative;
- stress or bereavement;
- a form of anger against the circumstances of life.

Environmental factors include:

- lack of easy access to a lavatory (eg lavatory upstairs);
- inadequate lighting and heating in the lavatory;
- lack of handrails and aids to ensure that the lavatory seat is at the right level;
- concern about arrangements during the night and reluctance to use a commode;
- inability to get out of bed at night and use the commode;
- concern about any lack of privacy, particularly when help has to be given in toileting arrangements;
- difficulties in removing clothing in time.

ACTION YOU CAN TAKE TO IMPROVE CONTINENCE

1 Encourage attention to diet and adequate intake of food and drink.

NOTE Do not restrict intake of liquids during the day, other than alcohol, as this can lead to dehydration. Avoid taking too many drinks in the evening, before going to bed.

2 Try to ensure that any drugs prescribed are taken as indicated.

3 Encourage regular visits to the lavatory and, in particular, at bed times. (Part of a continence programme.)

4 Try to ensure that lavatory facilities are within easy reach.

5 Encourage independence in the use of the lavatory.

6 Afford as much privacy as possible when helping the sufferer to the lavatory.

7 Arrange for the provision of mobility aids if it is difficult to reach the toilet in time.

8 Avoid too much preoccupation with the condition and paying too much unnecessary attention to it.

9 Avoid any form of conflict over the condition – that will only make the situation worse.

10 Keep the sufferer clean and dry.

11 Work with others involved – for example, the GP, nurse, continence adviser – to maintain an agreed continence programme (as it is called).

12 Advise health staff if there are any changes in the condition.

SOURCES OF HELP

You should never feel isolated and unsupported in any aspect of the care you provide, and this applies to the challenging area of maintaining continence and improving incontinence. Help and support should be available from the following sources/people.

- Health service staff, particularly district nurses, occupational therapists and continence advisers, who are now employed by many health authorities.

- On a practical level, supplies of various aids, such as special clothing, pads, pants, waterproof sheets, commodes, raised lavatory seats, drawsheets and mattresses, should be available from the health service or, in some cases, from the local authority SSD.

- Handrails may need to be fitted, or special toilet seats installed.

- Clothing that can be unfastened quickly and easily may help.

- Exercises can strengthen bladder control. Information on these may be obtained from the district nurse and/or physiotherapist who should meet the sufferer and assess their need.

- Where sufferers have to be fitted with a catheter, help and advice on management will come from health service staff.

- Your own agency may have guidelines on maintaining continence, which should be easily available. Check with your line manager.

- Training should be available for home care staff working with people suffering with incontinence.

Generally:

- Always help the sufferer in a way that will maintain their privacy and dignity at all times.

- Do not discuss the person's incontinence with a third person present unless they are there to give medical advice.

- **Never** blame the sufferer when accidents occur nor make them feel embarrassed or ashamed in any way when you are changing pads or washing them.

- **Never** let the sufferer feel that you find these activities distasteful. Be aware of the feelings that may be experienced owing to incontinence – fear of reprimand, shame, embarrassment, loss of self-control and loss of dignity. Acknowledge them as sensitively as possible. To ignore them could increase the problem.

- Try to reassure the sufferer that incontinence does not damage the respect that they deserve as an individual.

CASE STUDY 1

Mr M, in his mid-70s, lived with his daughter in a house with an upstairs toilet. For some years he had experienced increasing difficulty in passing urine. He got to the point where he had to go very frequently during both day and night; he rarely thought that he had emptied his bladder; urine flow was retarded and slow. He got little warning before needing to go to the toilet. Sometimes he began to pass urine before he reached the toilet or his underwear became stained because he 'dribbled' after emptying his bladder.

He became miserable and ashamed of this; he worried that his daughter might find out about what he considered to be his urinary incontinence. He was a very private man who did not like the idea of discussing his problem with anyone, least of all with his daughter. She was aware of his difficulties but did not feel comfortable about mentioning it to him.

His daughter had a job that required occasional travel abroad. On these occasions a Home Care Assistant was provided to help Mr M. The Home Care Assistant became so concerned about Mr M's condition that he asked Mr M whether he had sought help. For the first time, Mr M was able to unburden himself about what he considered to be a shameful situation. The Home Care Assistant persuaded Mr M to see his GP; he was referred to hospital and was treated for the effects of an enlarged prostate gland. After convalescence, his 'problem' was very much improved.

Questions

1   *What individual skills do you think the Home Care Assistant used?*

2   *What does the case study tell you about communication in the M family?*

3   *Why do you think that for some people a problem like this is 'shameful', while other people would think little of it and see a GP as soon as the condition became troublesome?*

4   *If the problem had not been so easily resolved, how do you think Mr M could have been helped?*

CASE STUDY 2

Mr O was relatively fit until he suffered a severe stroke in his late 60s. After a lengthy stay in hospital, he returned home but, despite attempts at rehabilitation, he remained severely disabled and doubly incontinent (of urine and of stool). His wife, who was some years younger than Mr O, was capable of looking after him and became his main and virtually constant carer. Mr O's double incontinence was, however, a source of great difficulty to both of them. Despite continuing medical intervention, the condition did not improve and the couple were very distressed by the prospect of a dismal future.

Help was provided and a Home Care Assistant and a nurse with skills in dealing with incontinence were assigned on a regular basis to provide advice, practical help and support to the Os. This included the provision of incontinence pads and other aids, and a toileting programme/routine was devised aimed at trying to improve the situation.

Mr O remained doubly incontinent but his condition did improve, as did his mental and physical health. The situation for Mr and Mrs O remained difficult but the help they received made life much easier for them.

Questions

1 *What individual skills do you think the Home Care Assistant used in caring for Mr O and in supporting Mrs O?*

2 *Should Mr O have been cared for elsewhere? If so, where?*

3 *What arrangements might have been made to try to ensure that Mrs O did not 'break down' in her difficult situation?*

KEY POINTS

- Incontinence can often be cured or at least improved. It should never be accepted as an inevitable part of growing old.
- People are frequently embarrassed and ashamed about being incontinent. You should show tact and sympathy, and understanding and acceptance of the reasons for it.
- Take appropriate action to minimise the effect of incontinence.
- Seek assistance from the incontinence adviser and other health service professionals.

9 Sexuality and Older People

This chapter identifies some of the issues relating to personal sexual relationships, particularly among older people, and how they may impinge on your work as a Home Care Assistant.

THE NEED FOR PERSONAL RELATIONSHIPS

People of all ages have needs for emotional and sexual expression that are normally met through a wide range of different relationships.

Older people have the same rights as any other citizens to make and maintain friendships and personal relationships without interference or censure. Many will still have access to rewarding relationships and the opportunities, through leisure activities, to make new relationships.

Many people who are housebound, however, experience extreme loneliness and emotional deprivation. They have few, if any, opportunities to express their emotions or make new rewarding relationships. You should be aware of their need for emotional expression. You can show warmth and affection by using touch, such as a pat on the hand or shoulder when appropriate, to indicate to them that they are valued in their own right.

SEXUALITY

Contrary to what might be believed, older people do have sexual feelings and can enjoy sex as much as anyone else. Sexual activity is one of life's great pleasures and it is not solely the province of the young, as most Home Care Assistants find out for themselves in the course of their work.

Older people, particularly those living on their own, may have a need to express and find outlets for their feelings. You should not be surprised, therefore, if some people you are caring for wish to talk about sexual matters or if signs of sexual activity are in evidence around the home. You should show tact and discretion in responding, discouraging the person only if their behaviour becomes unacceptable – for example, if a man you are caring for exposes himself to you.

There are two particular aspects relating to the sexuality of the people you are caring for. First there is their individual, personal need for sexual satisfaction. Secondly is the way in which this is expressed, which may affect or impinge on you, the Home Care Assistant.

You need to recognise the sexual needs of people but this should never mean that you are expected to put up with or condone unacceptable behaviour or expression. Only you can decide what you personally consider to be unacceptable behaviour.

Your employing organisation should have a written policy on equal opportunities and sexual harassment. Obtain a copy and find out how it relates to your work as a Home Care Assistant. You should receive training on these issues.

Some people may behave inappropriately and without any inhibitions because of learning disabilities or dementia. You should discuss any such difficulties with your line manager. People with learning disabilities may be helped by referral for specialist counselling.

There are a number of specialist organisations that may be able to help and advise younger people with physical disabilities.

GENERAL POINTS OF GUIDANCE

- Always respect a person's privacy. Knock **and wait** to be invited in before entering bedrooms, bathrooms and other private rooms.

- Don't over-react or be judgemental about what you might find in the home in the way of pornographic material, sex aids, dolls. If they are left on public display, you can politely ask for them to be put away, out of sight. If they are persistently left out, report the matter to your line manager.

- Be careful about the 'signals' you send to the person. Don't joke about sexual matters or make suggestive comments or innuendos – your motives might be misunderstood.

- If you are propositioned in any way, politely and firmly refuse. If it continues in an unacceptable way, inform your line manager.

- If you are subjected to sexual touching, ask the person to stop their unacceptable behaviour and inform your line manager. It is not unknown for female carers either to have to go in twos to the homes of some male users or to have to be replaced by a male carer.

- Be careful how and where you touch people, particularly when providing intimate care.

- If you unexpectedly find someone engaged in a sexual activity – leave quickly and discreetly.

- Don't accept any form of sexual harassment. If it persists, inform your line manager.

If at any stage you feel out of your depth or uncomfortable with the way in which the person expresses their sexual and emotional needs (eg if pornographic material offends you or if you think it is unlawful), discuss it with your line manager.

Everyone has their own individual and different tolerance to and views of sexual matters and materials. These views should be respected, both for you and the person you are caring for. However, clearly sexual advances cannot be tolerated and should be reported to your line manager, as should any form of sexual harassment. This is an issue that requires sensitive handling in terms of initial response and subsequent management.

CASE STUDIES

1   **Miss L** was a bright old lady of 89 but she required a Home Care Assistant to help her with shopping and housework. One day, the Home Care Assistant returned to Miss L's house and found her semi-naked on the settee with an elderly neighbour. The Home Care Assistant excused herself, closed the door quickly and retired in some confusion. Her brief view of the couple indicated to her that they were engaged in sexual activity.

2   **A Home Care Assistant** had been allocated to provide help to Miss E, a young severely disabled woman who lived alone in a flat, supported intensively by a range of domiciliary services. One afternoon, the Home Care Assistant walked into the bedroom of Miss E and found her and a disabled friend apparently attempting to have sexual intercourse on the bed. The couple were not at all embarrassed and asked the Home Care Assistant if she would help them.

3   **A Home Care Assistant** had just started work at the home of an elderly man. He was relatively able but had begun to neglect himself and his home. The Home Care Assistant went to his bedroom and found that he had a blow-up life-sized doll in the bed. It was obviously used for sexual comfort. The Home Care Assistant felt very uncomfortable about having to clean the room with the doll 'looking on'.

4   **A young female Home Care Assistant** was working in a small unit in the community tenanted by three young men with severe learning disabilities. They were in receipt of a number of domiciliary services. One of the men developed the habit of masturbating in her presence. Although he did not otherwise try to compromise her, she found his behaviour upsetting.

Questions

1   *What individual skills do you think the Home Care Assistant(s) needed to use in caring for the people referred to above?*

2   *What would you have done if faced with these situations?*

3   *What are the dangers for Home Care Assistants in any of these situations?*

4   *From where might Home Care Assistants expect to receive support when encountering situations like these?*

5   *Should Home Care Assistants be expected to suppress or impose their own*
    moral standards when dealing with situations like these?

KEY POINTS

- Home Care Assistants should be aware of the need that people have, in particular those who are housebound, for emotional expression.
- Older people can enjoy sex just as much as younger people.
- Use tact and discretion in responding to signs of sexual activity.
- Never put up with unacceptable sexual behaviour or sexual harassment. Report it to your line manager.
- Be careful what signals you give out. Don't joke about sexual matters or flirt. Your motives may be misunderstood.

10 Financial Matters

This chapter considers issues relating to the personal finances of people receiving care, including charging for the service. It explores the level of involvement that Home Care Assistants should have with the personal finances of those they are caring for and what happens if people are unable to look after their own finances themselves.

PERSONAL FINANCE

People receiving care should always be encouraged to take full responsibility for handling their own financial affairs and have the right to choose and control how their money is spent. Some people, however, although capable of managing their own affairs, receive assistance from relatives, friends or solicitors.

Someone who is physically frail and housebound may choose to:

1   Draw up a mandate, authorising another person to use their bank or building society account to carry out essential transactions.

2   Authorise an agent to act on their behalf – for example, with the agreement of their employing organisation, authorising a Home Care Assistant to collect their pension by signing the appropriate slip in the pension book.

3   Appoint another person, generally a relative or a solicitor, to act on their behalf through a 'Power of Attorney'.

4 Authorise another person, generally a relative, to act as the 'Appointee' on their behalf, to make claims and receive benefits on behalf of the claimant from the local Benefits Agency (Social Security office).

Inevitably you will find that you almost always have to deal with money belonging to the person you are caring for, even if it is only the fairly basic level of shopping, reading bills for someone who has poor vision, paying bills or collecting pensions. It is clearly an area where difficulties can arise and you should be aware of the need to be *extremely careful*.

Responsible agencies employing Home Care Assistants should have their own guidance on money matters. If you belong to a trade union, this may also be a source of specific advice. ACE Books have published a helpful reference book, *Managing Other People's Money*, by Penny Letts (see p 154). The following general guidelines are intended to warn you about the potential pitfalls, bearing in mind that you might be dealing with the finances of people who may be forgetful, vulnerable or confused.

LEVEL OF INVOLVEMENT

Shopping, paying bills and collecting pensions are of considerable help to many people. These tasks are an accepted part of the work of the Home Care Assistant, where it has been assessed as a care need and is part of the care plan.

Any further involvement beyond this level (eg using banking services, making withdrawals from Post Office Savings or building society accounts) should be resisted. Any request that you undertake more than basic financial transactions on behalf of the person you are caring for should be discussed with your line manager.

PROVIDING FINANCIAL ADVICE

You may find that the people you are caring for need advice and assistance in budgeting. Advice may be offered on how to allocate weekly spending to cover essential items such as food, fuel bills, rent, etc, and ways explored of spreading the payment of bills by (for example) the purchase of TV, telephone or electricity stamps or other similar budget payment schemes.

When purchasing items on someone else's behalf, each item should be discussed, including its general availability, where to buy it and the likely cost. This is particularly important if the person has been housebound for some time and has no recent experience of shopping for the items concerned. You should make alternative suggestions, if appropriate, so that the person can make an informed choice on how to spend their money.

Dealing with money can be a particularly sensitive area when the person has severe sight loss. You might ask them to take the money out of their purse themselves and hand it to you. Similarly when giving back change, it is advisable to count it back into the person's hand so that they know exactly what change you have given them. The Royal National Institute for the Blind provides aids to assist people with poor sight to identify their money.

VALUABLE POSSESSIONS

Everyone has the right to dispose of their own personal valuables, such as jewellery, as they wish. Some may have made arrangements with banks for safe-keeping. Others may not be aware of the value of their possessions and leave them around the home for everyone to see.

If you are worried about the security of valuable items or of large sums of money kept in the house, you should discuss it first with the person concerned – including the possible physical danger to themselves as a result of theft and burglary. This should be done calmly and factually, without causing any alarm but alerting them to the dangers they are placing themselves in.

If you continue to be worried, the situation should be discussed with your line manager and, with the agreement of the person concerned, with their relatives.

Accepting gifts

Many of the people you are caring for will be very grateful for your help, support and care, and will wish to show their gratitude. You must be very, very careful about accepting gifts. You will need to use your discretion in deciding whether or not to accept gifts. To refuse could give offence, but to accept a too extravagant or expensive gift could be interpreted as improper conduct. Your employing organisation may have a specific policy relating to the acceptance of gifts – find out if they have.

In general, acceptance of a small, modest gift on birthdays or at Christmas should not be misconstrued. If you are in doubt, discuss it with your line manager.

If the person you are caring for suggests mentioning you in their Will, you should take positive steps to discourage them and inform your line manager. To seek a bequest in their Will would be quite improper.

INABILITY TO MANAGE PERSONAL FINANCES

Some people may be or become unable to manage their own financial affairs because of confusion or other mental disability. In these cases arrangements will have to be made for others to act on their behalf. The person taking responsibility for the financial affairs may be a relative, friend or solicitor. However, if there is no-one able or willing to undertake the duties of an attorney or a receiver (whichever is appropriate in the circumstances) you will need to contact the local authority to enquire if a member of their staff undertakes these roles for people in this position. (See following section on 'Enduring Power of Attorney'.)

It is a major decision to remove a person's right to manage and handle their own finances and must never be taken lightly. Every effort must be made to safeguard their best interest.

You may consider that someone you are caring for is reaching the stage of confusion where they are unable to handle their finances. Report this to their relatives and to your line manager, who will, if necessary, arrange for an assessment (including a psychiatric assessment) to be made by the appropriate people.

Enduring Power of Attorney

Any arrangements the person had previously made for managing their affairs such as an ordinary Power of Attorney (see section on 'Personal Finance' above) will cease to be valid, unless an Enduring Power of Attorney (EPA) order has been made.

An EPA should be created while the person (the 'donor') is still capable of understanding the nature and effect of creating such a document when it is explained to them. For example, the 'donor' should know that the attorney will be able to assume complete authority over their *financial* affairs and will be able to continue to deal with these matters even when the donor is no longer able to supervise the attorney's actions. If the donor is able to understand the role of an EPA, the fact that the donor may, at the same time, be 'incapable by reason of mental disorder of managing and administering their property and affairs' does not affect the validity of the EPA. The EPA should be registered with the Court of Protection as soon as it has been signed by the donor and the attorneys.

The EPA can come into effect immediately it has been signed by the donor and attorney, or after it has been registered with the Court of Protection, depending upon the wording of the EPA. In either case, as soon as the attorney has reason to believe that the person is or is becoming mentally disordered, the attorney *must* apply to the Court of Protection to have the EPA registered. It is not necessary to have the mental incapacity formally diagnosed.

There are likely to be an increasing number of cases where it is possible to provide support to enable people to live at home, but who cannot manage their own personal finances.

If the person has assets, it will be necessary to apply to the Court of Protection. If the person's assets are small, the Court of Protection may issue a Short Procedure Order enabling someone to deal with these. However, if the assets are substantial, the Court has the power to appoint a Receiver to control and manage the person's finances and property on their behalf. It is likely that a member of the person's family would be appointed as the Receiver.

As the Home Care Assistant you will be in a position to provide valuable information about the person you are caring for and about their physical and mental condition. However, if you are concerned, it should be discussed with your line manager, who can ensure that appropriate steps are taken. You should not take direct action yourself in these circumstances.

If there is no relative or friend willing and able to act as Receiver, the court will appoint a solicitor. Application proceedings are slow but may be speeded up in certain circumstances.

Further information on management of financial affairs is provided in Age Concern England's Factsheet 22 (details on p 157)

CHARGING FOR THE SERVICE

Most social services departments make some charge for the provision of home care. This may be:

a a flat rate charge to all regardless of how many hours of service are actually provided;

b a tiered charge dependent upon the number of hours of service provided;

c a tiered charge dependent upon the income of the person needing care and their ability to pay.

Most local authorities do not charge people for the service if they are on Income Support.

In general it will be the care manager who will undertake the financial assessment as part of the care plan and package. It will be their responsibility to ensure that the person fully understands what they should pay and signs the necessary forms, before you commence providing the care service.

Nevertheless, whether you are employed by the social services department, or your organisation is contracted to provide services on behalf of the SSD, or you are employed and paid privately for the care you provide, you should be aware of the basis upon which the charges are made to the person you are caring for.

People receiving care are entitled to a full explanation of the mechanism for charging for the service. They also have the right to choose whether or not to have the service, on the basis of cost.

WELFARE RIGHTS

Many people may be entitled to benefits such as Income Support or Housing or Attendance Allowance. Because you are frequently the one person who is in most regular contact with the person needing care, you will often be asked for advice and information on a wide range of subjects.

You should check with the person that they are aware of all the possible entitlements. This may have been undertaken originally by the care manager when assessing need, but benefits and entitlement change. You can help by obtaining relevant information leaflets on their behalf and, if appropriate, making contact with welfare rights advisers, the Department of Social Security and other agencies giving specialist advice.

The ACE Books' annual publication *Your Rights* (see p 154) gives detailed information on the money benefits to which older people may be entitled.

CHECKLIST – FINANCIAL MATTERS

- Do not mix up your own personal money with that of the person you are caring for. Keep their money entirely separate from your own.
- Always keep a careful record of the money given to you.
- Do get receipts for the foods and anything else you buy on behalf of those you are caring for.
- 'Settle up' the account as soon as possible and give the person the receipts. Itemise all the transactions and take the person through them carefully. Don't leave it all until the end of the week, when the person may have forgotten about the transactions.
- Don't borrow money or anything else from people you are caring for or lend them money, and don't talk about your own financial affairs.
- Don't buy from or sell anything to someone you are caring for.
- Don't accept gifts other than very small tokens such as chocolates or soap, etc which might be exchanged at Christmas.

- If someone insists on giving you money as a mark of appreciation, consult your line manager

- Don't suggest – even as a joke – that someone should remember you in their Will. If you are told that you are to be a beneficiary in the Will of someone you are caring/have cared for, advise your line manager.

- Report to your line manager immediately if you are accused by the client/family/friends of stealing money or any other item, or any other dishonesty

- Report to your line manager if you think someone you are caring for is being the victim of dishonesty by a third person or persons.

- Don't ask anyone you care for to be a guarantor for a hire purchase application.

- If you find large amounts of cash about the home, advise your line manager – but no one else!

- Exercise strict confidentiality about everything you might know about someone else's financial affairs.

CASE STUDIES

1   **A Home Care Assistant** was working with an older man. She went to his home one day to be confronted by a very angry relative of the client, who accused her of stealing £200 which he said had been left in a jar in the kitchen. The Home Care Assistant denied stealing the money, and both she and the client were very upset. The police became involved and began to investigate the accusation. The Home Care Assistant advised her supervisor and her trade union official. While the matter was being investigated, the Home Care Assistant was suspended from duty. Two days after the accusation was made, the money was found intact in another part of the house. The Home Care Assistant was reinstated but requested that she should be moved. The client was very upset by the incident, for which he blamed himself. He was also upset at the loss of his carer whose services he valued.

2   **A Home Care Assistant** had worked with a woman, Mrs P, for over two years. During this time the Home Care Assistant began increasingly to have financial difficulties and she discussed her problem with Mrs P in such a way as to make her feel that she ought to help. The Home Care Assistant accepted a series of small 'loans' amounting to just over £50.

Mrs P's daughter learned of this and informed the employing agency. As a result, the Home Care Assistant was suspended while the matter was investigated; after a disciplinary hearing, the Home Care Assistant was dismissed. Mrs P was very upset about this. She considered that she could do what she wanted with her own money. She was angry with her daughter for 'interfering' and thereby depriving her of a carer and a friend.

3　**Mr L, a young Home Care Assistant** working with an older forgetful man, became concerned about the attention paid to the client by two of his teenage grandchildren. They were often at the house and were 'borrowing' money from their grandfather. This went on for some time and the client, who relied on a State pension, seemed never to have any money. The Home Care Assistant reported the matter to his supervisor who first of all went to see the client. He became very upset and said it was family business and not the concern of 'outsiders'. When the situation did not improve, a case conference was called, attended by the Home Care Assistant, and it was decided that the family should be advised. This was done and caused a great deal of trouble among the family members. The agency was told that Mr L should not work any longer with the client.

4　**Mrs C, a Home Care Assistant**, had worked with Mr T, an older single man for six years. They had developed a very good relationship and Mr T had become very fond of his carer. After a while, Mr T told Mrs C that he intended to leave her his money and was making a Will to this effect. He said that, although he had relatives, he wanted Mrs C to have his money because 'You have looked after me better than they ever have'. Mrs C informed her supervisor of this as soon as possible. The supervisor discussed it with the agency's legal adviser and, as a result, Mr T's solicitor was approached and made aware of the situation from the agency's point of view. Mr T's solicitor said that, in her view, there was no evidence that her client was being coerced. On the contrary, he seemed very happy with his decision and had made it clear that he wanted Mrs C to benefit from his Will. The situation was therefore accepted. Two years later, Mr T died and left Mrs C £57,000.

Questions

1　*What individual skills do you think the Home Care Assistant needed to use in caring for the people referred to above?*

2   *What would you have done if faced with these situations?*

3   *What ethical issues are raised by these cases?*

KEY POINTS

- You need to be aware of the basis on which people are charged for the care service you provide.

- People receiving care should be encouraged to take on responsibility for their own financial affairs.

- You need to handle money on behalf of those you are caring for with the utmost care and caution. You should resist getting involved in their financial matters other than shopping, paying bills and collecting their pension.

- The people you are caring for will look to you as a source of information on a wide range of financial matters, benefits and welfare rights. You need to know where to go to obtain the information they seek.

- It is natural that the people you care for will wish to show their appreciation but you should only ever accept small and modest gifts. To accept expensive gifts could be considered improper conduct. Not to accept small gifts could give offence.

- Resist any suggestion that you should be mentioned in someone's will and report it to your line manager.

- Never mix your own finances and personal money with those of someone you are caring for.

11 Terminal Illness and Death

This final chapter looks briefly at some of the points to note in providing home care to people who are terminally ill. This is skilled, specialist work which you should not be expected to undertake unless you have considerable experience of working as a Home Care Assistant and have completed an appropriate training programme.

PROVIDING CARE FOR THOSE WHO ARE TERMINALLY ILL

Perhaps the most difficult thing you will be asked to do as a Home Care Assistant will be to care for someone who is terminally ill. It is common for Home Care Assistants to become very close to the people they are caring for, and coping with the long terminal illness of a friend can place stress and many pressures on you.

It is often very important to the dying person and their relatives that they are allowed to stay at home until the end. It is essential that care is provided with dignity and compassion. Comfort may be given by skilled physical care, including holding the person's hand and other appropriate touching, and listening and speaking in a calm manner.

You should not be alone in providing care. It should be shared with others, such as health staff and the person's own family and friends. Specialist services may be involved, such as Macmillan nurses and Marie Curie Cancer Care.

Caring for people who are terminally ill is skilled work. It is essential that a consistent approach is adopted. You should not find yourself being expected to provide care for people who are terminally ill without having been given in advance the necessary guidance, training and briefing on the particular individual situation.

Points to note for guidance:

- The aim should be to make the person as comfortable as possible – in mind as well as in body.

- Watch for symptoms of pain so that medical help can be summoned as often as necessary to ensure the person's continued comfort.

- In many cases now, the person will know of their condition and may need to talk about it and their impending death. Most Home Care Assistants are sympathetic listeners and can play an important role in helping people and their personal carers to express fears about death and dying, and about other anxieties such as concern for those left behind. Talking about death should not be treated with embarrassment or brushed aside.

  Family members often find it easier to talk about these issues and the situation to someone who is from outside the family.

  Think how you feel about talking to someone about death. If you think it will be difficult or distressing, talk to your line manager about it first.

- The terminally ill person may wish to be involved in their own funeral arrangements. If they have no close family, you should be prepared to be involved in this process and to behave as naturally as is possible.

- If the person is **not** aware of their situation or the severity of their condition, you should **never** tell them.

- You will need ready access to advice and guidance as the condition of the person deteriorates; for example, medical assistance in pain control and any other distressing symptoms of the illness.

- The person you are caring for may very likely express a strong wish to remain at home. All concerned in the care of the person – including you, the Home Care Assistant – should do everything possible to comply with this wish. However, there will be occasions when this is just not possible.

- The aim of all those involved in terminal care should be to make the life of the person as comfortable and fulfilling as possible.

- There should be no forced jollity or contrived optimism, particularly if someone is aware of the eventual outcome of the condition. A simple open approach is best in helping the person to retain their dignity.

- The preferences of the person and the family with regard to treatment, religious observance and cultural practices should be ascertained and carefully followed.

- As death approaches, the person should not be left alone. Where requested by the person or their family, either at the time or before, the appropriate religious leader should be summoned.

- News of the death should be given to the family, GP and others as soon as possible in a dignified manner.

- Grief and mourning should not be hidden, but it should be accepted that some people may not openly display their emotions.

- Staff who care for people who are dying are likely to be under considerable stress and need particular support. The problems of providing terminal care should be freely discussed among staff.

If, as a Home Care Assistant, you are involved in providing care for people who are terminally ill, you should expect and, if necessary, request support from your line manager. Everyone involved in providing care for the dying person – family, friends and Home Care Assistants – will need support, and perhaps counselling, after the death. This is perfectly natural.

CASE STUDIES

1 **Mrs G**, a 63-year-old woman suffering from inoperable cancer, was cared for in her own home by a team of health and social services staff and a Macmillan nurse. She was very ill and sometimes in a lot of pain. Despite this, she wanted to remain at home and rejected suggestions that she be admitted to a hospice. The team of care staff, including two Home Care Assistants, continued their support for Mrs G until she died. They enabled her to stay in her house and remain relatively pain free and comfortable.

2 **Two Home Care Assistants** began to look after Mr R after he had a severe stroke. His condition did improve but, nevertheless, he remained disabled. With the help of his carers and a district nurse, he was able to remain in his flat. After three and a half years of continuous care, he had another stroke, from which he did not recover. Both the Home Care

Assistants had grown very fond of Mr R and regarded him as a good friend. They were deeply affected by his death.

3 **Mr and Mrs W** had been married for over 50 years and were devoted to each other. Although they had become physically frail, they were supported at home by two Home Care Assistants sharing seven-day care and providing help with food shopping and house cleaning. Mr W suffered a severe heart attack and died after two days in hospital. Mrs W was distraught both at the death of her husband and at its suddenness. She required medical help and the support of her two Home Care Assistants, who were themselves very upset at the death of Mr W.

Questions

1 *What individual skills do you think the Home Care Assistants needed to use in caring for the people referred to above?*

2 *What support do you consider Home Care Assistants should have in coming to terms with their own feelings at the loss of people they have cared for?*

3 *Do you think Home Care Assistants should specialise in the care of terminally ill people?*

KEY POINTS

- Caring for people who are terminally ill is specialised and demanding work but can be very rewarding.
- As a Home Care Assistant you should not be working on your own but as part of a team which includes specialist nursing and medical help as required, as well as the person's own family.
- You will need to provide care with dignity and compassion.
- The aim of the care is to make the remaining life of the dying person as comfortable and fulfilling as possible.
- Following the death, all concerned will need help and support. Family and friends will be distressed and will often turn to the Home Care Assistant for support, as someone outside of the family.
- The Home Care Assistant may be distressed and in need of support from their line manager and colleagues.

Appendix 1

Charter of Rights for People Receiving Home Care

(Reproduced with thanks to Surrey County Council)

1 The right to remain in their own home, if that is their wish.
2 The right to retain their chosen life-style.
3 The right to have their personal dignity respected, irrespective of physical or mental disability.
4 The right to be treated as an individual in their own right, whatever their physical or mental disability.
5 The right to personal independence, personal choice and personal responsibility for actions, including acceptance of risk.
6 The right to personal privacy for themselves, their belongings and their affairs.
7 The right to have cultural, religious, sexual and emotional needs accepted and respected.
8 The right to have care appropriate to their needs from suitably trained and experienced staff.
9 The right to have, and to participate in, regular reviews of their individual circumstances, and to have a friend and adviser present if they so wish.
10 The right to participate as fully as possible in the formulating of their own individual care plans.
   The right to be fully informed about the services provided by the organisation, and of any decisions made by the authority's staff that may affect their personal well-being.

12 The right of access to personal files.

13 The right of access to a formal complaints procedure and to be represented by a friend or adviser if they so wish.

14 The right to be represented by an advocate if they so wish, or are unable to make personal representation through mental incapacity.

Appendix 2

Checklist – Policies and Practices of the Employing Organisation

The Home Care Assistant works in difficult, challenging and generally isolated circumstances. You therefore need all the help and assistance you can get, and it is unreasonable for any employing agency to expect you to work in a vacuum.

The employing agency should itself provide a basis and a framework for the provision of home care by supplying the following information on the organisation's policies and practices to every Home Care Assistant.

You may like to place a tick alongside those you have copies of:

- Aims and objectives of the organisation.
- Conditions of employment, including travel expenses and rights to join a trade union.
- Job description, including the activities required to be undertaken.
- Clarification of activities you are *not* supposed to undertake.
- Information on the care plan for each service user (if compiled); alternatively, information on (assessed) care needs of each service user.
- The provision of non-discriminatory practice.
- Equal opportunities and sexual harassment.
- Quality assurance and service standards.
- Complaints procedure.
- Confidentiality of information.
- Health and safety regulations, including accident report procedure.

- Data protection and subject access.
- Charging policy of the organisation.
- Handling and administering medicines.
- Lifting and handling.
- Handling money and finance (on behalf of service user).
- Accepting gifts/legacies from service users.

It is unreasonable and irresponsible of any employing organisation to expect any of their Home Care Assistants to undertake their work efficiently and effectively without such basic information and 'ground rules'.

Appendix 3

Checklist – Issues or Situations to be Referred to Others for Guidance or Action

The following occurrences or situations should always be discussed or reported to the appropriate person – generally your line manager or the manager of your employment agency.

1 Home Care in Context

- When the care needs have changed due to an improvement/deterioration in condition, or there is a change in the circumstances and a reassessment is required.
- Any example of discrimination that gives cause for concern.

2 Enter You, the Home Care Assistant

- Any possibility that a person and/or the family will make a formal complaint – for whatever reason.

3 The Basic Skills of Home Care Assistants

- Any difference in expectation between the tasks the Home Care Assistant expects to undertake (from the care plan and/or care assessment) and what the person and/or their personal carer or family want.
- Clarification, if necessary, of the tasks the Home Care Assistant is not expected to undertake.
- Any potentially dangerous hazards in the home (see also Chapter 6).

- Any person you are caring for who refuses to bathe (refer to the district nurse and/or occupational therapist).
- Any suspicion of unacceptable or criminal practices involving the vulnerable person needing care and their family or friends; for example, physical abuse or coercion.

4 The Health of Older People

- Changes in the person's physical condition. If the person agrees, report the changes to the GP or district nurse, or to your line manager if there is no such agreement forthcoming.
- Deterioration in psychological condition, signs of depression, loss of appetite, sleep, etc.
- Signs of onset of confusion.
- Any request from the person, the GP or the district nurse to assist with medication.
- Any refusal to take medication.
- Aggressive or violent attacks from the person or their family/friends.

5 Eating and Nutrition

You need to refer to your line manager, and then to a GP or district nurse, if any of the people you are caring for is:

- refusing to eat;
- not keeping to a medically required diet;
- possibly drinking greater amounts of alcohol than is good for them;
- experiencing difficulty eating (when previously they didn't).

6 Accidents and Emergencies, including Health and Safety

- Any accident, medical and/or emergency situation.
- If you arrive at the home, cannot get in and there is no reply.
- The onset of dirt and infestation.

7 Mobility and Disability

- Any need for special equipment to facilitate mobility.

- If toenails need cutting or if corns or bunions need treatment.
- If pressure sores are developing as a result of lack of mobility.

8 Maintaining Continence

- Evidence that a person is losing continence. (The district nurse or GP should also be informed.)
- Anything that the agency may be able to provide to assist in the maintenance of continence; for example, help with soiled clothing, fitting aids and adaptations.

9 Sexuality and Older People

- Persistent sexual harassment in any form, such as intimate touching, propositioning, etc.
- Any form of sexual behaviour that is unacceptable to the Home Care Assistant, even if it is the result of disabilities such as Alzheimer's disease or learning disabilities.

10 Financial Matters

- Any request to be more involved with the person's financial affairs beyond shopping, collecting pension and paying bills (eg authorisation to use the person's bank account on their behalf).
- Any wish the person may express to give gifts or money to the Home Care Assistant, or to remember him or her in their will.
- Any accusation of dishonesty on the part of the Home Care Assistant, by the person, or their family or friends.
- Fears that the person may be the victim of dishonesty by a third party.
- Concern if the person leaves valuable possessions or large amounts of money around the home.
- Concern about the person's capacity to handle their own financial affairs.

11 Terminal Illness and Death

- Summon medical help if the person is in pain.
- Recognise the need for personal support and advice to help you through a stressful situation.

Appendix 4

Checklist – Providing a Quality Service

1. Home Care in Context

- Treat each person you care for as a separate individual with his or her own particular needs and situation.

- Recognise the **rights** of each person and ensure that the values for service provision are put into practice in your work.

- Recognise the importance of maintaining **confidentiality**.

- If you are providing care to a person from an ethnic minority community you should understand their particular needs and respect their cultural and religious requirements.

- People with care needs and their family should be involved in decisions relating to the care they receive and given choice in the nature of and way in which the care services are provided.

- Ensure that the people you are caring for are aware of your organisation's complaints procedure but take all action necessary to put things right first time.

2 Enter You, the Home Care Assistant

- Obtain all the information you need on the person and their care needs, including who else (other agencies) is providing care, before making the first visit.

- Your first visit to the home should be planned and structured, and follow an agreed procedure.

- Learn as much as you can about the person's wants, needs and preferences from any family carers.

- Recognise that the wants and needs of the family carer are separate and different from those of the person needing care.

- Understand the importance of good communication skills, and always adopt good communication practice that is appropriate to the particular needs of the person you are caring for and any disabilities they may possess.

- Never make assumptions about the way to address the person you are caring for and their family. Always ask them how they prefer to be addressed.

- Make a list of sources of assistance, which can be kept in a prominent place in the home.

3 Basic Skills of Home Care Assistants

- Always be aware that you are working in someone else's home and treat it accordingly.

- Respect the person's home and possessions. Treat them with care.

- Never smoke while in someone else's home and don't eat or drink unless specifically invited to do so.

- Support and maintain the person's independence as far as possible. Encourage them to do as much as possible for themselves.

- Vary the level of care to reflect changes in the person's needs, level of ability and changing circumstances.

- Do not impose your standards on the person you are caring for. Obtain permission before making changes in the home.

- Always adopt safe working practices. Identify potential hazards to the safety of the person as well as to yourself.

- Be aware of the need for hygienic working practices and wear protective clothing and rubber gloves.

- Undertake the basic activities, taking account of the need to apply good caring skills.

- Wherever possible, Home Care Assistants should be recruited from the same ethnic community as the person needing care.

- Know and recognise when situations give cause for concern and report them to the appropriate person.

4 The Health of Older People

- Never assume that becoming older automatically means that people become ill. Always respond to people according to their condition and not according to their age.

- Recognise that you must take into account the social and emotional needs as well as the physical needs of the person and act accordingly.

- Take action to reduce social and emotional isolation.

- Observe standard hygiene procedures to protect you and the person you are caring for against the spread of infection.

- Be alert for symptoms of hypothermia.

- Encourage the person and remind them when to take medication, but assist in administering medication only with the full knowledge of a member of the medical professional and (unless you are self-employed) your line manager.

5 Eating and Nutrition

- Recognise the importance of food and meal times, particularly for people who are housebound. Provide advice on healthy eating, a balanced diet and nutrition.

- Always observe strict hygiene precautions when handling food.

- People should always choose what they want to eat. They should also be involved as much as possible in shopping and in cooking and preparing food.

- Seek advice on the availability of special equipment and aids that make it easier for people with disabilities to prepare food, open cans and feed themselves (for example).

- Encourage and support people who are on special diets for medical or other reasons.

- Take time with people while they are eating their meal; provide any assistance necessary as requested by them.

6 Health and Safety, including Accidents and Emergencies

- Always observe safe working practices, in the interest of the person you are caring for as well as your own.
- Identify possible hazards in the home and try to persuade the person to take appropriate action.
- Ensure that you receive training in lifting and handling techniques, but never try to lift people or bulky and heavy objects yourself.
- Be familiar with the correct emergency procedures in a variety of situations.
- Have first-aid training.
- Take all appropriate precautions to secure the home.
- Recognise when a home is becoming insanitary and/or infested.

7 Mobility and Disability

- Mobility is essential to maintain independence. Find appropriate ways of encouraging people to be as mobile as possible.
- Recognise the importance of exercise in maintaining the health of people you are caring for.
- Encourage people and their family carers to take care of the feet and to wear properly fitting shoes rather than slippers.
- Know where to go for information on aids and equipment to assist mobility.

8 Maintaining Continence

- Deal with matters relating to incontinence with great sensitivity.
- Recognise that incontinence can frequently be cured or at least improved, and encourage the person and/or their family carer to seek help and advice.
- Assist the person to maintain a positive continence programme.

9 Sexuality and Older People

- Recognise the need everyone has for emotional fulfilment and social relationships, and behave and respond appropriately in each separate and different situation.

- Be careful about the signals you give. Don't joke about sexual matters or make suggestive comments. Your motives may be misunderstood.

10 Financial Matters

- Be able to refer the person to the appropriate agency to get financial advice.
- Always clarify with the person exactly how much of their money you have spent and always give them receipts.
- Always keep the person's money entirely separate from your own.
- Never accept gifts from the person you are caring for.
- Be aware of the basis of charging for the service you provide and recognise that the service user has a right to a full explanation of the costs.

11 Terminal Illness and Death

- You should not be asked to provide care for someone who is terminally ill unless you are experienced as a Home Care Assistant and have received the appropriate training
- You will work as part of a team which will include family, friends and professional medical staff such as the district or community nurse.
- You need to recognise the personal stress that such work will cause, and seek support from your line manager and colleagues.

Appendix 5

Checklist – Training as a Home Care Assistant

All newly appointed Home Care Assistants should be provided with induction training. This should include guidance on the organisation's policies and practices (see Appendix 2).

All subsequent training should be competence based and assessed in practice, in accordance with the requirements of the National Vocational Qualification (NVQ). The following competency units in the NVQ Integrated Care awards relate to chapters in this book.

Chapter 1	O	**Chapter 7**	W4, X8–X10, X13–X15,
Chapter 2	W1, V1, V2		Z5–Z7, Z9–Z11
Chapter 3	X1, X2, Y1, Z5–Z13, Z19	**Chapter 8**	Z9, Z11, Z12
Chapter 4	U4, U5, W4, X13, X14,	**Chapter 9**	W1, W2, W5, Y2, Z1, Z3
	Y4, Z4, Z7, Z8	**Chapter 10**	V1, Y1–Y3, Z2
Chapter 5	Y1, Z1	**Chapter 11**	W2, Z8, Z14, Z15, Z19
Chapter 6	Y2, Z1, Z5, Z8		

For information on the NVQ in Care and in the Integrated Health and Personal Social Services Care Awards, contact:

**Occupational Standards Council
for Health and Social Care
(Care Sector Consortium)**
13–16 Russell Square
London WC1B 5EP

Tel: 071-636 6811

In-service training topics should include the following.

Essential

- Basic values that should underpin the provision of care.
- The provision of non-discriminatory services and practice.
- Health and safety.
- Lifting and handling.
- Communication skills – including people who are hearing impaired.
- The process of ageing.
- Basic first aid.
- Common disabilities and diseases, including hypothermia.
- Awareness of the effect of visual impairment (partial sight).
- Standards to be attained in the delivery of services.

Desirable

- Maintaining continence.
- Dealing with aggressive behaviour.
- Caring for confused people.

Specialist training

- Caring for people who are terminally ill.
- Caring for people from ethnic minority communities – their particular needs.
- The tasks of a nursing auxiliary (eg changing dressings; pressure sores).
- Working in dirty and/or infested homes.

Training material

Other useful training material and packages include the following, available from the Local Government Management Board (address on p 149):

A Friend in Deed – resource training material for Home Care Assistants;

Look Closer – See ME – video and training material on aggression and older people.

Appendix 6

Some Common Illnesses and Disabilities of Later Life

Alcohol abuse This can be a lifelong habit or start in retirement. Older alcohol abusers may fall frequently and become confused, incontinent or malnourished. They may become isolated and lonely if friends and family avoid them when they are unpleasant after drinking.

Outlook No one can be compelled to stop drinking; people who have done so to excess all their lives, rarely change their behaviour in old age. All carers can do is to try to reduce the dangers of and damage from their chosen life-style in whatever ways they can. People who 'take to drink' in later life can sometimes be helped, and may control their drinking if their health and social circumstances are improved.

Alzheimer's disease This is a form of dementia, a degenerative disease of the brain. Usually it is noticed in someone around the age of 80, and the cause is not known. A few of the rare cases that start before the age of 60 show an inherited pattern.

Outlook People with Alzheimer's disease do not get better and usually get worse, though how fast this happens varies from one person to another. There is no cure for the disease, but good medical care helps to control symptoms and to keep the sufferer as well as possible.

Arthritis There are several forms of this joint disease; the commonest is osteoarthritis (OA). Pain, stiffness and reduced mobility can be helped by: pain-relieving medicines; a balance of rest and exercise; warmth, as from a heating pad; and assessment by an occupational therapist and provision of equipment; physiotherapy; surgery to replace affected joints.

Outlook   Arthritis is a painful nuisance but does not shorten life and only rarely becomes severe enough to interfere with independent living.

Angina (pectoris)   Angina is a tight, squeezing chest pain caused by narrowing of the coronary arteries that supply the heart with blood. The pain may be brought on by exertion or emotion and is relieved by rest and prescribed medicines.

Outlook   People with angina are at increased risk of suffering a heart attack. However, they can be helped by treatment and should be encouraged to keep as active as possible within the limits of their pain.

Breathing problems   These can be due to chronic bronchitis, emphysema or asthma in any combination. Some people are severely disabled by breathlessness all the year round, whilst others become much worse in the winter because of chest infections.

Outlook   This depends on the severity of the condition. Stopping smoking will always help, and it is never too late to do so. Chest infections need prompt treatment with antibiotics; a 'chesty' person whose spit becomes green or yellow needs to see the doctor urgently.

Brittle bones (osteoporosis)   The bones become weaker as the years pass, especially in women after the menopause. The softened vertebrae in the spine may become squashed, causing pain and stooping. Weakened hip and wrist bones may break easily.

Outlook   Osteoporosis is not in itself dangerous, though it reduces independence and enjoyment of life. Some people who break their hips die of complications. Hormone replacement therapy helps to prevent osteoporosis in women.

Cancer   This happens when body cells multiply rapidly to form a tumour. Some cancers are said to be 'malignant' because they spread rapidly to other organs, causing serious disease and death. Others spread more slowly, and a person can live for years with them before dying of something else.

Outlook   Very variable, depending on the type of cancer. Early diagnosis is important because early treatment may slow spread or even give a complete cure. Treatment can be by surgery, radiotherapy or drugs in any combination; though effective in the long run, this can cause serious unwanted effects in the short term. Advanced cancer can cause severe symptoms such as pain or breathlessness, and special skills of a hospice outreach team or a Macmillan nurse may be needed to keep the sufferer comfortable.

Dementia   The dementias are a group of degenerative diseases of the brain, causing gradual loss of intellectual abilities and emotional skills. The commonest types are Alzheimer's disease and multi-infarct dementia, a form of stroke illness.

Outlook   People with dementia get worse as time passes, though the rate of decline varies from person to person. It is important to make sure that the symptoms are not due to a curable physical illness, as there is no medical cure for dementia. Good general care can greatly improve the sufferer's quality of life, and respite care may relieve relatives and help them to go on caring.

Diabetes   In this condition the body is unable to process sugar properly because insulin is in short supply or the body has become insensitive to it. Older people usually develop a type of diabetes that can be controlled by diet and tablets without the need for insulin injections.

Outlook   Complications can cause disability from heart, blood vessel and kidney disorders. Sight can deteriorate, and unnoticed and untreated skin ulcers lead to gangrene. Good control of diabetes makes these complications less likely, so you should encourage your clients to follow their treatment plans carefully. Regular eye checks and skilled chiropody are especially important.

Hearing problems   These have many causes and should never be attributed to normal ageing; full assessment is required.

Outlook   This depends on the cause. Medication may be helpful, and the person should be given advice and equipment to help them make the most of their remaining hearing.

HIV/AIDS   The Human Immunodeficency Virus (HIV) is passed from one person to another in infected body fluids. This usually involves unprotected sex, use of contaminated injection equipment or passage of the virus from mother to baby before or during birth. The risks to those caring for people with AIDS are very small.

Outlook   People who are positive for HIV develop the illnesses that form the AIDS complex, the Acquired Immunodeficiency Syndrome. Many of these happen because the person's resistance to infection is low. Eventually these illnesses prove fatal.

Hypothermia This is the condition in which central body temperature is low. Older people are vulnerable because their body's ability to control temperature deteriorates. Especially at risk are those who: have mobility problems or a tendency to fall; abuse alcohol; are mentally ill or mentally frail; are on low incomes; are isolated, with few visitors. With hypothermia, a person becomes sleepy and confused and a covered part of the body such as the armpit or abdomen feels cold to the touch. (For how to help, see p 66.)

Outlook This depends on the circumstances; it is worse if the person has a severe underlying illness or has become very cold.

Malnutrition This can be caused by lack of teeth, by poor diet because of deficiency in shopping and cooking or lack of money, or by illnesses that interfere with the digestion and absorption of food.

Outlook This depends on the cause, which should be identified and put right whenever possible. Vitamins and other food supplements are sometimes necessary as a last resort.

Mental health problems Common ones in later life include depression, dementia (see above) and paranoid states. People with *depressive disorder* are preoccupied by gloomy thoughts, have no enjoyment of life and feel hopeless about the future. They may be slowed down and apathetic, or overactive and constantly seeking reassurance. They may complain of physical symptoms such as headache or abdominal pain but no physical explanation can be found. They are at risk from self-neglect or from deliberate self-harm: you should *always* report a client's suicidal thoughts to the doctor and/or your line manager.

Outlook People with depressive disorder can be helped by medical treatment, by psychotherapy and by improvement in their health and social circumstances. It is often overlooked in older people, so you should watch out for the signs.

Paranoid states People with paranoid states wrongly believe that others are a threat to them or their property. They become very anxious and may try to retaliate to their imagined injuries. Many people with this problem lead solitary lives and have problems with sight and hearing; they commonly suffer with tinnitus (noises in the ear).

Outlook Treatment is often helpful, but it may be difficult to get the patient to accept it. The community psychiatric nurse is often helpful in persuading the sufferer to have the treatment and in giving advice and support to carers.

Parkinson's disease This is a disorder of the nervous system, and affects the ability to move. Older sufferers complain mainly of stiffness and difficulty in moving about and walking, while tremor is more pronounced in younger people.

Outlook Medicines can be very helpful, but must always be taken exactly as prescribed; treatment may need to be adjusted by a specialist from time to time. Changing meal times or giving vitamins may interfere with the actions of drugs and make the person ill. Physiotherapy and speech therapy are sometimes helpful. Some Parkinson's sufferers develop a form of dementia.

Sight problems These have many causes and should never be attributed to normal ageing; full assessment is required.

Outlook This depends on the cause. Surgery and/or medicines may be helpful, and the person should be given advice and equipment to help them make the most of remaining sight.

Strokes These happen when part of the brain loses its blood supply. They can be minor, moderately severe or massive and fatal. Multi-infarct dementia is the result of a series of small strokes.

Outlook This depends on how badly the brain is damaged, how well the person is rehabilitated and whether they have other disabilities that will limit recovery. The effect on the person depends on which parts of the brain are damaged and how badly: one common problem is of weakness and loss of feeling down one side of the body, loss of vision to that side and sometimes difficulty in speaking or in understanding what is said.

Appendix 7

Sources of Further Information

Associations

Alzheimer's Disease Society
2nd floor, Gordon House
10 Greencoat Place
London SW1P 1PH
Tel: 071-306 0606

Arthritis Care
18 Stephenson Way
London NW1 2HD
Tel: 071-916 1500

Association for Continence Advice
Dean Centre
Castle Farm Road
Newcastle upon Tyne NE3 1PH
Tel: 091-213 0050 (2.00–7.00 pm)

Association of Crossroads Care Attendant Schemes
10 Regent Place
Rugby
Warwickshire CV21 2PN
Tel: 0788 73653

BACUP (British Association of Cancer United Patients)
3 Bath Place
London EC2A 3JR
Tel: 071-613 2121

British Association of Domiciliary Care Officers (BADCO)
Maggie Utley
2 St Catherine's Close
Sindlesham
Wokingham
Berkshire RG11 5BZ
Tel: 0734 798888

Carers National Association
20–25 Glasshouse Yard
London EC1A 4JS
Tel: 071-490 8818

Citizens Advice Bureaux
Look in local telephone directory
under Citizens Advice Bureaux

Community Health Councils
Look in local telephone directory
under the name of the
Community Health Council
where you live

Contact
15 Henrietta Street
London WC2E 8HQ
Tel: 071-240 0630

Counsel and Care for the Elderly
Lower Ground floor
Twyman House
16 Bonny Street
London NW1 9PG
Tel: 071-485 1566

Cruse Bereavement Care
126 Sheen Road
Richmond
Surrey TW9 1UR
Tel: 081-940 4818

Disabled Living Foundation
380–384 Harrow Road
London W9 2HU
Tel: 071-289 6111

Help The Aged
16–18 St James' Walk
London EC1R 0BE
Tel: 071-253 0253

Incontinence Information Helpline
(Newcastle) 091-213 0050

Joint Initiative for Community Care Ltd
6 Minerva Gardens
Wavendon Gate
Milton Keynes MK7 7SR
Tel: 0908 585373

National Council of Domiciliary Care Services (NCDCS)
Tad Kubisa, Chairman NCDCS
Director of Social Services
Castle Court, Shire Hall
Cambridge CB3 0AP

Parkinson's Disease Society of the UK
72 Upper Woburn Place
London WC1H 0RA
Tel: 071-383 3513

Partially Sighted Society
Queen's Road
Doncaster
South Yorkshire DN1 2NX
Tel: 0302 368998

Royal National Institute for Deaf People
105 Gower Street
London WC1E 6AH
071-387 8033

Royal National Institute for the Blind
224 Great Portland Street
London W1N 6AA
Tel: 071-388 1266

Social Care Association (SCA)
23A Victoria Road
Surbiton
Surrey KT6 4JZ,
Tel: 081-390 6831

Standing Committee for Ethnic Minority Senior Citizens
5 Westminster Bridge Road
London SE1 7XW
Tel: 071-928 0095

United Kingdom Home Care Association (UKHCA)
22 Southway
Carshalton
Surrey SM5 4HW
Tel: 081-770 3658

Health Service

NHS Training Directorate
St Bartholomews Court
18 Christmas Street
Bristol BS1 5BT
Tel: 0272 291029

Local Government

Local Government Management Board
Arndale House
Arndale Centre
Luton LU1 2TS
Tel: 0582 451166

Trade Union

UNISON
1 Mabledon Place
London WC1II 9AJ
Tel: 071-388 2366

Further Reading

Community Care – General

Caring for People – Community Care in the Next Decade and Beyond, Department of Health White Paper (HMSO, 1989).

Department of Health Policy Guidance (HMSO, 1990).

Home Care

Caring Jobs. Leaflet on job opportunities in local government. Available from the LGMB at the address given on p 149.

Good Care – A guide to the good care of people living at home (Kent County Council Social Services Department, Springfield, Maidstone, Kent ME14 2LW).

Service Quality in Home Care, report of seminar, March 1990 (Social Services Inspectorate, Department of Health).

Standards for Registration for Domiciliary Care, Joint Advisory Group of Domiciliary Care Association. Available from JICC Ltd, 6 Minerva Gardens, Wavendon Gate, Milton Keynes MK7 7SR.

Taking Good Care: A handbook for care assistants by Jenyth Worsley (Age Concern England, 1989).

Other Useful Publications

Community Life: A code of practice for community care (1990) and *Home Life: A code of practice for residential care* (1984) [substantial overlap with issues relevant to home care provision]. Both available from Centre for Policy on Ageing, 25–31 Ironmonger Row, London EC1V 3PQ.

Health and Healthy Living – A Guide for Older People Department of Health (HMSO, 1991).

About Age Concern

CareFully is one of a wide range of publications produced by Age Concern England – National Council on Ageing. In addition, Age Concern is actively engaged in training, information provision, research and campaigning for retired people and those who work with them. It is a registered charity dependent on public support for the continuation of its work.

Age Concern England links closely with Age Concern centres in Scotland, Wales and Northern Ireland to form a network of over 1,400 independent local UK groups. These groups, with the invaluable help of an estimated 250,000 volunteers, aim to improve the quality of life for older people and develop services appropriate to local needs and resources. These include advice and information, day care, visiting services, transport schemes, clubs, and specialist facilities for physically and mentally frail older people.

Age Concern England
1268 London Road
London SW16 4ER
Tel: 081-679 8000

Age Concern Scotland
54a Fountainbridge
Edinburgh EH3 9PT
Tel: 031-228 5656

Age Concern Wales
4th Floor
1 Cathedral Road
Cardiff CF1 9SD
Tel: 0222 371566

Age Concern Northern Ireland
3 Lower Crescent
Belfast BT7 1NR
Tel: 0232 245729

Publications from ◆C◆ Books

A wide range of titles is published by Age Concern England under the ACE Books imprint.

Health and Care

The Community Care Handbook: The new system explained
Barbara Meredith

The provision of care in the community is changing as a result of recent legislation. Written by one of the country's foremost experts, this book explains in practical terms why the reforms were necessary, what they are, how they will work and whom they will affect.

£11.95   0 86242-121-7

The 36-Hour Day: A family guide to caring at home for people with Alzheimer's disease and other confusional illnesses
Nancy L Mace and Peter V Rabins MD

The new edition of this highly successful guide covers the medical, legal, financial and emotional aspects of caring, combining practical advice with specific examples.

Co-published with Headway

£9.99   0–34056–382–6

Taking Good Care: A handbook for care assistants
Jenyth Worsley

Written for all those concerned with caring for older people, this book covers such vital issues as communication skills, the medical and social problems encountered by carers, the role of the assistant, the resident's viewpoint and activities and group work.

£6.95   0–86242–072–5

General

Living, Loving and Ageing: Sexual and personal relationships in later life

Wendy Greengross and Sally Greengross

Sexuality is often regarded as the preserve of the younger generation. This book, for older people and those who work with them, tackles the issues in a straightforward fashion, avoiding preconceptions and bias.

£4.95   0–86242–070–9

Eating Well on a Budget

Sara Lewis

Completely revised, the new edition of this successful title offers sound advice on shopping and cooking cost-effectively and includes wholesome original recipes for four complete weekly menus.

£5.95   0–86242–120–9

Money Matters

Managing Other People's Money

Penny Letts

The management of money and property is usually a personal and private matter. However, there may come a time when someone else has to take over on either a temporary or a permanent basis. This book looks at the circumstances in which such a need could arise and provides a step-by-step guide to the arrangements which have to be made.

£5.95   0–86242–090–3

Your Rights

Sally West

A highly acclaimed annual guide to the State benefits available to older people. Contains current information on Income Support, Housing Benefit and retirement pensions, among other sources of financial help, and provides advice on how to claim them.

Further information on application.

Housing

Housing Options for Older People

David Bookbinder

A review of housing options is part of growing older. All the possibilities and their practical implications are carefully considered in this comprehensive guide.

£4.95   0–86242–108–X

To order books, please send a cheque or money order, payable to Age Concern England, to the address below. Postage and packing are free. Credit card orders may be made on 081-679 8000.

Age Concern England (DEPT C)
PO Box 9
London SW16 4EX

SERVICE-RELATED BOOKLETS FROM AGE CONCERN

Community Care Changes

A series of five booklets on aspects of community care legislation and how to help your organisation thoroughly address these issues, £17.00 for the set or:

Complaints £1.95

Community Care Plans £2.75

Quality and Inspection £5.00

Purchasing and Contracting £5.00

Assessment and Care Management £5.00

Information is presented through a question and answer format.

Contracts and the Contract Culture

An introductory guide to assess the pros and cons of contracting for voluntary organisations and the questions you need to ask yourselves and the potential contractor. £5.00

Speak up for Yourself

Aims to provide a basic understanding of what advocacy means and to outline how the philosophy may be reflected in practice. £2.00

Standards in Day Care Services

Covers a range of services related to day care and how standards can be set and monitored. £7.50

Orders under £10 for service-related booklets should include a cheque payable to Age Concern England. Orders over £10 can be invoiced.

For further information or to order any of the above booklets, contact:

Fieldwork Services Unit
Age Concern England
1268 London Road
London SW16 4ER

Tel: 081-679 8000 ext 2304

INFORMATION FACTSHEETS

Age Concern England produces over 30 factsheets on a variety of subjects. Among these the following titles may be of interest to readers of this book:

Factsheet 6 *Finding Help at Home*

Factsheet 10 *Local Authority Charging Procedures for Residential and Nursing Home Care*

Factsheet 11 *Preserved Entitlement to Income Support for Residential and Nursing Homes*

Factsheet 22 *Legal Arrangements for Managing Financial Affairs*

Factsheet 29 *Finding Residential and Nursing Home Accommodation*

Factsheet 32 *Disability and Ageing: Your Rights to Social Services*

To order factsheets

Single copies are available free on receipt of a 9" x 6" sae. If you require a selection of factsheets or multiple copies totalling more than five, charges will be given on request.

A complete set of factsheets is available in a ring binder at the current cost of £34, which includes the first year's subscription. The current cost for annual subscription for subsequent years is £14. There are different rates of subscription for people living abroad.

Factsheets are revised and updated throughout the year and membership of the subscription service will ensure that your information is always current.

For a free list of all factsheets, or to order copies, send a large sac to:

Information and Policy Department
Age Concern England
1268 London Road
London SW16 4ER

Index